Science 110

Teacher's Guide

CONTENTS

Author: **Alpha Omega Publications**
Editor: Alan Christopherson, M.S.

Alpha Omega Publications®

804 N. 2nd Ave. E., Rock Rapids, IA 51246-1759

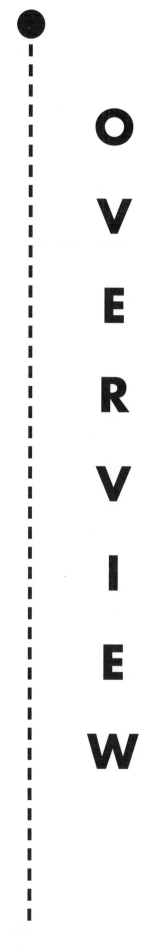

OVERVIEW

SCIENCE

Curriculum Overview
Grades 1–12

Science LIFEPAC Overview

	Grade 1	Grade 2	Grade 3
LIFEPAC 1	**YOU LEARN WITH YOUR EYES** • Name and group some colors • Name and group some shapes • Name and group some sizes • Help from what you see	**THE LIVING AND NONLIVING** • What God created • Rock and seed experiment • God-made objects • Man-made objects	**YOU GROW AND CHANGE** • Air we breathe • Food for the body • Exercise and rest • You are different
LIFEPAC 2	**YOU LEARN WITH YOUR EARS** • Sounds of nature and people • How sound moves • Sound with your voice • You make music	**PLANTS** • How are plants alike • Habitats of plants • Growth of plants • What plants need	**PLANTS** • Plant parts • Plant growth • Seeds and bulbs • Stems and roots
LIFEPAC 3	**MORE ABOUT YOUR SENSES** • Sense of smell • Sense of taste • Sense of touch • Learning with my senses	**ANIMALS** • How are animals alike • How are animals different • What animals need • Noah and the ark	**ANIMAL AND ENVIRONMENT CHANGES** • What changes an environment • How animals are different • How animals grow • How animals change
LIFEPAC 4	**ANIMALS** • What animals eat • Animals for food • Animals for work • Pets to care for	**YOU** • How are people alike • How are you different • Your family • Your health	**YOU ARE WHAT YOU EAT** • Food helps your body • Junk foods • Food groups • Good health habits
LIFEPAC 5	**PLANTS** • Big and small plants • Special plants • Plants for food • House plants	**PET AND PLANT CARE** • Learning about pets • Caring for pets • Learning about plants • Caring for plants	**PROPERTIES OF MATTER** • Robert Boyle • States of matter • Physical changes • Chemical changes
LIFEPAC 6	**GROWING UP HEALTHY** • How plants and animals grow • How your body grows • Eating and sleeping • Exercising	**YOUR FIVE SENSES** • Your eye • You can smell and hear • Your taste • You can feel	**SOUNDS AND YOU** • Making sounds • Different sounds • How sounds move • How sounds are heard
LIFEPAC 7	**GOD'S BEAUTIFUL WORLD** • Types of land • Water places • The weather • Seasons	**PHYSICAL PROPERTIES** • Colors • Shapes • Sizes • How things feel	**TIMES AND SEASONS** • The earth rotates • The earth revolves • Time changes • Seasons change
LIFEPAC 8	**ALL ABOUT ENERGY** • God gives energy • We use energy • Ways to make energy • Ways to save energy	**OUR NEIGHBORHOOD** • Things not living • Things living • Harm to our world • Caring for our world	**ROCKS AND THEIR CHANGES** • Forming rocks • Changing rocks • Rocks for buildings • Rock collecting
LIFEPAC 9	**MACHINES AROUND YOU** • Simple levers • Simple wheels • Inclined planes • Using machines	**CHANGES IN OUR WORLD** • Seasons • Change in plants • God's love never changes • God's Word never changes	**HEAT ENERGY** • Sources of heat • Heat energy • Moving heat • Benefits and problems of heat
LIFEPAC 10	**WONDERFUL WORLD OF SCIENCE** • Using your senses • Using your mind • You love yourself • You love the world	**LOOKING AT OUR WORLD** • Living things • Nonliving things • Caring for our world • Caring for ourselves	**PHYSICAL CHANGES** • Change in man • Change in plants • Matter and time • Sound and energy

Grade 4	Grade 5	Grade 6	
PLANTS • Plants and living things • Using plants • Parts of plants • The function of plants	**CELLS** • Cell composition • Plant and animal cells • Life of cells • Growth of cells	**PLANT SYSTEMS** • Parts of a plant • Systems of photosynthesis • Transport systems • Regulatory systems	LIFEPAC 1
ANIMALS • Animal structures • Animal behavior • Animal instincts • Man protects animals	**PLANTS: LIFE CYCLES** • Seed producing plants • Spore producing plants • One-celled plants • Classifying plants	**ANIMAL SYSTEMS** • Digestive system • Excretory system • Skeletal system • Diseases	LIFEPAC 2
MAN'S ENVIRONMENT • Resources • Balance in nature • Communities • Conservation and preservation	**ANIMALS: LIFE CYCLES** • Invertebrates • Vertebrates • Classifying animals • Relating function and structure	**PLANT AND ANIMAL BEHAVIOR** • Animal behavior • Plant behavior • Plant-animal interaction • Balance in nature	LIFEPAC 3
MACHINES • Work and energy • Simple machines • Simple machines together • Complex machines	**BALANCE IN NATURE** • Needs of life • Dependence on others • Prairie life • Stewardship of nature	**MOLECULAR GENETICS** • Reproduction • Inheritance • DNA and mutations • Mendel's work	LIFEPAC 4
ELECTRICITY AND MAGNETISM • Electric current • Electric circuits • Magnetic materials • Electricity and magnets	**TRANSFORMATION OF ENERGY** • Work and energy • Heat energy • Chemical energy • Energy sources	**CHEMICAL STRUCTURE** • Nature of matter • Periodic Table • Diagrams of atoms • Acids and bases	LIFEPAC 5
PROPERTIES OF MATTER • Properties of water • Properties of matter • Molecules and atoms • Elements	**RECORDS IN ROCK: THE FLOOD** • The Biblical account • Before the flood • The flood • After the flood	**LIGHT AND SOUND** • Sound waves • Light waves • The visible spectrum • Colors	LIFEPAC 6
WEATHER • Causes of weather • Forces of weather • Observing weather • Weather instruments	**RECORDS IN ROCK: FOSSILS** • Fossil types • Fossil location • Identifying fossils • Reading fossils	**MOTION AND ITS MEASUREMENT** • Definition of force • Rate of doing work • Laws of motion • Change in motion	LIFEPAC 7
THE SOLAR SYSTEM • Our solar system • The big universe • Sun and planets • Stars and space	**RECORDS IN ROCK: GEOLOGY** • Features of the earth • Rock of the earth • Forces of the earth • Changes in the earth	**SPACESHIP EARTH** • Shape of the earth • Rotation and revolution • Eclipses • The solar system	LIFEPAC 8
THE PLANET EARTH • The atmosphere • The hydrosphere • The lithosphere • Rotation and revolution	**CYCLES IN NATURE** • Properties of matter • Changes in matter • Natural cycles • God's order	**ASTRONOMY AND THE STARS** • History of astronomy • Investigating stars • Major stars • Constellations	LIFEPAC 9
GOD'S CREATION • Earth and solar system • Matter and weather • Using nature • Conservation	**LOOK AHEAD** • Plant and animal life • Balance in nature • Biblical records • Records of rock	**THE EARTH AND THE UNIVERSE** • Plant systems • Animal systems • Physics and chemistry • The earth and stars	LIFEPAC 10

	Grade 7	Grade 8	Grade 9
LIFEPAC 1	**WHAT IS SCIENCE** • Tools of a scientist • Methods of a scientist • Work of a scientist • Careers in science	**SCIENCE AND SOCIETY** • Definition of science • History of science • Science today • Science tomorrow	**OUR ATOMIC WORLD** • Structure of matter • Radioactivity • Atomic nuclei • Nuclear energy
LIFEPAC 2	**PERCEIVING THINGS** • History of the metric system • Metric units • Advantages of the metric system • Graphing data	**STRUCTURE OF MATTER I** • Properties of matter • Chemical properties of matter • Atoms and molecules • Elements, compounds, & mixtures	**VOLUME, MASS, AND DENSITY** • Measure of matter • Volume • Mass • Density
LIFEPAC 3	**EARTH IN SPACE I** • Ancient stargazing • Geocentric Theory • Copernicus • Tools of astronomy	**STRUCTURE OF MATTER II** • Changes in matter • Acids • Bases • Salts	**PHYSICAL GEOLOGY** • Earth structures • Weathering and erosion • Sedimentation • Earth movements
LIFEPAC 4	**EARTH IN SPACE II** • Solar energy • Planets of the sun • The moon • Eclipses	**HEALTH AND NUTRITION** • Foods and digestion • Diet • Nutritional diseases • Hygiene	**HISTORICAL GEOLOGY** • Sedimentary rock • Fossils • Crustal changes • Measuring time
LIFEPAC 5	**THE ATMOSPHERE** • Layers of the atmosphere • Solar effects • Natural cycles • Protecting the atmosphere	**ENERGY I** • Kinetic and potential energy • Other forms of energy • Energy conversions • Entropy	**BODY HEALTH I** • Microorganisms • Bacterial infections • Viral infections • Other infections
LIFEPAC 6	**WEATHER** • Elements of weather • Air masses and clouds • Fronts and storms • Weather forecasting	**ENERGY II** • Magnetism • Current and static electricity • Using electricity • Energy sources	**BODY HEALTH II** • Body defense mechanisms • Treating disease • Preventing disease • Community health
LIFEPAC 7	**CLIMATE** • Climate and weather • Worldwide climate • Regional climate • Local climate	**MACHINES I** • Measuring distance • Force • Laws of Newton • Work	**ASTRONOMY** • Extent of the universe • Constellations • Telescopes • Space explorations
LIFEPAC 8	**HUMAN ANATOMY I** • Cell structure and function • Skeletal and muscle systems • Skin • Nervous system	**MACHINES II** • Friction • Levers • Wheels and axles • Inclined planes	**OCEANOGRAPHY** • History of oceanography • Research techniques • Geology of the ocean • Properties of the ocean
LIFEPAC 9	**HUMAN ANATOMY II** • Respiratory system • Circulatory system • Digestive system • Endocrine system	**BALANCE IN NATURE** • Photosynthesis • Food • Natural cycles • Balance in nature	**SCIENCE AND TOMORROW** • The land • Waste and ecology • Industry and energy • New frontiers
LIFEPAC 10	**CAREERS IN SCIENCE** • Scientists at work • Astronomy • Meteorology • Medicine	**SCIENCE AND TECHNOLOGY** • Basic science • Physical science • Life science • Vocations in science	**SCIENTIFIC APPLICATIONS** • Measurement • Practical health • Geology and astronomy • Solving problems

Grade 10	Grade 11	Grade 12	
TAXONOMY • History of taxonomy • Binomial nomenclature • Classification • Taxonomy	INTRODUCTION TO CHEMISTRY • Metric units and instrumentation • Observation and hypothesizing • Scientific notation • Careers in chemistry	KINEMATICS • Scalars and vectors • Length measurement • Acceleration • Fields and models	LIFEPAC 1
BASIS OF LIFE • Elements and molecules • Properties of compounds • Chemical reactions • Organic compounds	BASIC CHEMICAL UNITS • Alchemy • Elements • Compounds • Mixtures	DYNAMICS • Newton's Laws of Motion • Gravity • Circular motion • Kepler's Laws of Motion	LIFEPAC 2
MICROBIOLOGY • The microscope • Protozoan • Algae • Microorganisms	GASES AND MOLES • Kinetic theory • Gas laws • Combined gas law • Moles	WORK AND ENERGY • Mechanical energy • Conservation of energy • Power and efficiency • Heat energy	LIFEPAC 3
CELLS • Cell theories • Examination of the cell • Cell design • Cells in organisms	ATOMIC MODELS • Historical models • Modern atomic structure • Periodic Law • Nuclear reactions	WAVES • Energy transfers • Reflection and refraction of waves • Diffraction and interference • Sound waves	LIFEPAC 4
PLANTS: GREEN FACTORIES • The plant cell • Anatomy of the plant • Growth and function of plants • Plants and people	CHEMICAL FORMULAS • Ionic charges • Electronegativity • Chemical bonds • Molecular shape	LIGHT • Speed of light • Mirrors • Lenses • Models of light	LIFEPAC 5
HUMAN ANATOMY AND PHYSIOLOGY • Digestive and excretory system • Respiratory and circulatory system • Skeletal and muscular system • Body control systems	CHEMICAL REACTIONS • Detecting reactions • Energy changes • Reaction rates • Equilibriums	STATIC ELECTRICITY • Nature of charges • Transfer of charges • Electric fields • Electric potential	LIFEPAC 6
INHERITANCE • Gregor Mendel's experiments • Chromosomes and heredity • Molecular genetics • Human genetics	EQUILIBRIUM SYSTEMS • Solutions • Solubility equilibriums • Acid-base equilibriums • Redox equilibriums	CURRENT ELECTRICITY • Electromotive force • Electron flow • Resistance • Circuits	LIFEPAC 7
CELL DIVISION & REPRODUCTION • Mitosis and meiosis • Asexual reproduction • Sexual reproduction • Plant reproduction	HYDROCARBONS • Organic compounds • Carbon atoms • Carbon bonds • Saturated and unsaturated	MAGNETISM • Fields • Forces • Electromagnetism • Electron beams	LIFEPAC 8
ECOLOGY & ENERGY • Ecosystems • Communities and habitats • Pollution • Energy	CARBON CHEMISTRY • Saturated and unsaturated • Reaction types • Oxygen groups • Nitrogen groups	ATOMIC AND NUCLEAR PHYSICS • Electromagnetic radiation • Quantum theory • Nuclear theory • Nuclear reaction	LIFEPAC 9
APPLICATIONS OF BIOLOGY • Principles of experimentation • Principles of reproduction • Principles of life • Principles of ecology	ATOMS TO HYDROCARBONS • Atoms and molecules • Chemical bonding • Chemical systems • Organic chemistry	KINEMATICS TO NUCLEAR PHYSICS • Mechanics • Wave motion • Electricity • Modern physics	LIFEPAC 10

MANAGEMENT

STRUCTURE OF THE LIFEPAC CURRICULUM

The LIFEPAC curriculum is conveniently structured to provide one teacher handbook containing teacher support material with answer keys and ten student worktexts for each subject at grade levels two through twelve. The worktext format of the LIFEPACs allows the student to read the textual information and complete workbook activities all in the same booklet. The easy to follow LIFEPAC numbering system lists the grade as the first number(s) and the last two digits as the number of the series. For example, the Language Arts LIFEPAC at the 6th grade level, 5th book in the series would be LAN0605.

Each LIFEPAC is divided into 3 to 5 sections and begins with an introduction or overview of the booklet as well as a series of specific learning objectives to give a purpose to the study of the LIFEPAC. The introduction and objectives are followed by a vocabulary section which may be found at the beginning of each section at the lower levels, at the beginning of the LIFEPAC in the middle grades, or in the glossary at the high school level. Vocabulary words are used to develop word recognition and should not be confused with the spelling words introduced later in the LIFEPAC. The student should learn all vocabulary words before working the LIFEPAC sections to improve comprehension, retention, and reading skills.

Each activity or written assignment has a number for easy identification, such as 1.1. The first number corresponds to the LIFEPAC section and the number to the right of the decimal is the number of the activity.

Teacher checkpoints, which are essential to maintain quality learning, are found at various locations throughout the LIFEPAC. The teacher should check 1) neatness of work and penmanship, 2) quality of understanding (tested with a short oral quiz), 3) thoroughness of answers (complete sentences and paragraphs, correct spelling, etc.), 4) completion of activities (no blank spaces), and 5) accuracy of answers as compared to the answer key (all answers correct).

The self test questions are also number coded for easy reference. For example, 2.015 means that this is the 15th question in the self test of Section II. The first number corresponds to the LIFEPAC section, the zero indicates that it is a self test question, and the number to the right of the zero the question number.

The LIFEPAC test is packaged at the centerfold of each LIFEPAC. It should be removed and put aside before giving the booklet to the student for study.

Answer and test keys have the same numbering system as the LIFEPACs and appear at the back of this handbook. The student may be given access to the answer keys (not the test keys) under teacher supervision so that he can score his own work.

A thorough study of the Curriculum Overview by the teacher before instruction begins is essential to the success of the student. The teacher should become familiar with expected skill mastery and understand how these grade level skills fit into the overall skill development of the curriculum. The teacher should also preview the objectives that appear at the beginning of each LIFEPAC for additional preparation and planning.

TEST SCORING and GRADING

Answer keys and test keys give examples of correct answers. They convey the idea, but the student may use many ways to express a correct answer. The teacher should check for the essence of the answer, not for the exact wording. Many questions are high level and require thinking and creativity on the part of the student. Each answer should be scored based on whether or not the main idea written by the student matches the model example. "Any Order" or "Either Order" in a key indicates that no particular order is necessary to be correct.

Most self tests and LIFEPAC tests at the lower elementary levels are scored at 1 point per question; however, the upper levels may have a point system awarding 2 to 5 points for various questions. Further, the total test points will vary; they may not always equal 100 points. They may be 78, 85, 100, 105, etc.

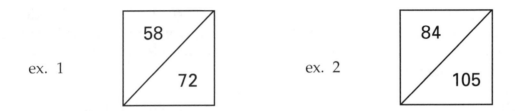

A score box similar to ex.1 above is located at the end of each self test and on the front of the LIFEPAC test. The bottom score, 72, represents the total number of points possible on the test. The upper score, 58, represents the number of points your student will need to receive an 80% or passing grade. If you wish to establish the exact percentage that your student has achieved, find the total points of his correct answers and divide it by the bottom number (in this case 72.) For example, if your student has a point total of 65, divide 65 by 72 for a grade of 90%. Referring to ex. 2, on a test with a total of 105 possible points, the student would have to receive a minimum of 84 correct points for an 80% or passing grade. If your student has received 93 points, simply divide the 93 by 105 for a percentage grade of 89%. Students who receive a score below 80% should review the LIFEPAC and retest using the appropriate Alternate Test found in the Teacher's Guide.

The following is a guideline to assign letter grades for completed LIFEPACs based on a maximum total score of 100 points.

LIFEPAC Test = 60% of the Total Score (or percent grade)
Self Test = 25% of the Total Score (average percent of self tests)
Reports = 10% or 10* points per LIFEPAC
Oral Work = 5% or 5* points per LIFEPAC
*Determined by the teacher's subjective evaluation of the student's daily work.

Example:

LIFEPAC Test Score	=	92%	92	x	.60	=	55 points
Self Test Average	=	90%	90	x	.25	=	23 points
Reports						=	8 points
Oral Work						=	4 points

TOTAL POINTS	=	90 points

Grade Scale based on point system:

100	–	94	=	A
93	–	86	=	B
85	–	77	=	C
76	–	70	=	D
Below		70	=	F

TEACHER HINTS and STUDYING TECHNIQUES

LIFEPAC Activities are written to check the level of understanding of the preceding text. The student may look back to the text as necessary to complete these activities; however, a student should never attempt to do the activities without reading (studying) the text first. Self tests and LIFEPAC tests are never open book tests.

Language arts activities (skill integration) often appear within other subject curriculum. The purpose is to give the student an opportunity to test his skill mastery outside of the context in which it was presented.

Writing complete answers (paragraphs) to some questions is an integral part of the LIFEPAC Curriculum in all subjects. This builds communication and organization skills, increases understanding and retention of ideas, and helps enforce good penmanship. Complete sentences should be encouraged for this type of activity. Obviously, single words or phrases do not meet the intent of the activity, since multiple lines are given for the response.

Review is essential to student success. Time invested in review where review is suggested will be time saved in correcting errors later. Self tests, unlike the section activities, are closed book. This procedure helps to identify weaknesses before they become too great to overcome. Certain objectives from self tests are cumulative and test previous sections; therefore, good preparation for a self test must include all material studied up to that testing point.

The following procedure checklist has been found to be successful in developing good study habits in the LIFEPAC curriculum.

1. Read the introduction and Table of Contents.
2. Read the objectives.
3. Recite and study the entire vocabulary (glossary) list.
4. Study each section as follows:
    a. Read the introduction and study the section objectives.
    b. Read all the text for the entire section, but answer none of the activities.
    c. Return to the beginning of the section and memorize each vocabulary word and definition.
    d. Reread the section, complete the activities, check the answers with the answer key, correct all errors, and have the teacher check.
    e. Read the self test but do not answer the questions.
    f. Go to the beginning of the first section and reread the text and answers to the activities up to the self test you have not yet done.
    g. Answer the questions to the self test without looking back.
    h. Have the self test checked by the teacher.
    i. Correct the self test and have the teacher check the corrections.
    j. Repeat steps a–i for each section.

5. Use the SQ3R* method to prepare for the LIFEPAC test.
6. Take the LIFEPAC test as a closed book test.
7. LIFEPAC tests are administered and scored under direct teacher supervision. Students who receive scores below 80% should review the LIFEPAC using the SQ3R* study method and take the Alternate Test located in the Teacher Handbook. The final test grade may be the grade on the Alternate Test or an average of the grades from the original LIFEPAC test and the Alternate Test.

    *SQ3R: **S**can the whole LIFEPAC.
                 Question yourself on the objectives.
                 Read the whole LIFEPAC again.
                 Recite through an oral examination.
                 Review weak areas.

GOAL SETTING and SCHEDULES

Each school must develop its own schedule, because no single set of procedures will fit every situation. The following is an example of a daily schedule that includes the five LIFEPAC subjects as well as time slotted for special activities.

Possible Daily Schedule

8:15	–	8:25	Pledges, prayer, songs, devotions, etc.
8:25	–	9:10	Bible
9:10	–	9:55	Language Arts
9:55	–	10:15	Recess (juice break)
10:15	–	11:00	Mathematics
11:00	–	11:45	Social Studies
11:45	–	12:30	Lunch, recess, quiet time
12:30	–	1:15	Science
1:15	–		Drill, remedial work, enrichment*

*Enrichment: Computer time, physical education, field trips, fun reading, games and puzzles, family business, hobbies, resource persons, guests, crafts, creative work, electives, music appreciation, projects.

Basically, two factors need to be considered when assigning work to a student in the LIFEPAC curriculum.

The first is time. An average of 45 minutes should be devoted to each subject, each day. Remember, this is only an average. Because of extenuating circumstances a student may spend only 15 minutes on a subject one day and the next day spend 90 minutes on the same subject.

The second factor is the number of pages to be worked in each subject. A single LIFEPAC is designed to take 3 to 4 weeks to complete. Allowing about 3-4 days for LIFEPAC introduction, review, and tests, the student has approximately 15 days to complete the LIFEPAC pages. Simply take the number of pages in the LIFEPAC, divide it by 15 and you will have the number of pages that must be completed on a daily basis to keep the student on schedule. For example, a LIFEPAC containing 45 pages will require 3 completed pages per day. Again, this is only an average. While working a 45 page LIFEPAC, the student may complete only 1 page the first day if the text has a lot of activities or reports, but go on to complete 5 pages the next day.

Long range planning requires some organization. Because the traditional school year originates in the early fall of one year and continues to late spring of the following year, a calendar should be devised that covers this period of time. Approximate beginning and completion dates can be noted on the calendar as well as special occasions such as holidays, vacations and birthdays. Since each LIFEPAC takes 3-4 weeks or eighteen days to complete, it should take about 180 school days to finish a set of ten LIFEPACs. Starting at the beginning school date, mark off eighteen school days on the calendar and that will become the targeted completion date for the first LIFEPAC. Continue marking the calendar until you have established dates for the remaining nine LIFEPACs making adjustments for previously noted holidays and vacations. If all five subjects are being used, the ten established target dates should be the same for the LIFEPACs in each subject.

FORMS

The sample weekly lesson plan and student grading sheet forms are included in this section as teacher support materials and may be duplicated at the convenience of the teacher.

The student grading sheet is provided for those who desire to follow the suggested guidelines for assignment of letter grades found on page 3 of this section. The student's self test scores should be posted as percentage grades. When the LIFEPAC is completed the teacher should average the self test grades, multiply the average by .25 and post the points in the box marked self test points. The LIFEPAC percentage grade should be multiplied by .60 and posted. Next, the teacher should award and post points for written reports and oral work. A report may be any type of written work assigned to the student whether it is a LIFEPAC or additional learning activity. Oral work includes the student's ability to respond orally to questions which may or may not be related to LIFEPAC activities or any type of oral report assigned by the teacher. The points may then be totaled and a final grade entered along with the date that the LIFEPAC was completed.

The Student Record Book which was specifically designed for use with the Alpha Omega curriculum provides space to record weekly progress for one student over a nine week period as well as a place to post self test and LIFEPAC scores. The Student Record Books are available through the current Alpha Omega catalog; however, unlike the enclosed forms these books are not for duplication and should be purchased in sets of four to cover a full academic year.

WEEKLY LESSON PLANNER

Week of:

	Subject	Subject	Subject	Subject
Monday				
	Subject	Subject	Subject	Subject
Tuesday				
	Subject	Subject	Subject	Subject
Wednesday				
	Subject	Subject	Subject	Subject
Thursday				
	Subject	Subject	Subject	Subject
Friday				

WEEKLY LESSON PLANNER

Week of:

	Subject	Subject	Subject	Subject
Monday				
	Subject	Subject	Subject	Subject
Tuesday				
	Subject	Subject	Subject	Subject
Wednesday				
	Subject	Subject	Subject	Subject
Thursday				
	Subject	Subject	Subject	Subject
Friday				

22

Student Name _____   Year _____

Bible

LP #	Self Test Scores by Sections 1	2	3	4	5	Self Test Points	LIFEPAC Test	Oral Points	Report Points	Final Grade	Date
01											
02											
03											
04											
05											
06											
07											
08											
09											
10											

History & Geography

LP #	Self Test Scores by Sections 1	2	3	4	5	Self Test Points	LIFEPAC Test	Oral Points	Report Points	Final Grade	Date
01											
02											
03											
04											
05											
06											
07											
08											
09											
10											

Language Arts

LP #	Self Test Scores by Sections 1	2	3	4	5	Self Test Points	LIFEPAC Test	Oral Points	Report Points	Final Grade	Date
01											
02											
03											
04											
05											
06											
07											
08											
09											
10											

Student Name _____   Year _____

Mathematics

LP #	Self Test Scores by Sections					Self Test Points	LIFEPAC Test	Oral Points	Report Points	Final Grade	Date
	1	2	3	4	5						
01											
02											
03											
04											
05											
06											
07											
08											
09											
10											

Science

LP #	Self Test Scores by Sections					Self Test Points	LIFEPAC Test	Oral Points	Report Points	Final Grade	Date
	1	2	3	4	5						
01											
02											
03											
04											
05											
06											
07											
08											
09											
10											

Spelling/Electives

LP #	Self Test Scores by Sections					Self Test Points	LIFEPAC Test	Oral Points	Report Points	Final Grade	Date
	1	2	3	4	5						
01											
02											
03											
04											
05											
06											
07											
08											
09											
10											

NOTES

INSTRUCTIONS FOR SCIENCE

The LIFEPAC curriculum from grades two through twelve is structured so that the daily instructional material is written directly into the LIFEPACs. The student is encouraged to read and follow this instructional material in order to develop independent study habits. The teacher should introduce the LIFEPAC to the student, set a required completion schedule, complete teacher checks, be available for questions regarding both content and procedures, administer and grade tests, and develop additional learning activities as desired. Teachers working with several students may schedule their time so that students are assigned to a quiet work activity when it is necessary to spend instructional time with one particular student.

The Teacher Notes section of the Teacher's Guide lists the required or suggested materials for the LIFEPACs and provides additional learning activities for the students. The materials section refers only to LIFEPAC materials and does not include materials which may be needed for the additional activities. Additional learning activities provide a change from the daily school routine, encourage the student's interest in learning and may be used as a reward for good study habits.

If you have limited facilities and are not able to perform all the experiments contained in the LIFEPAC curriculum, the Science Project List for grades 3-12 may be a useful tool for you. This list prioritizes experiments into three categories: those essential to perform, those which should be performed as time and facilities permit, and those not essential for mastery of LIFEPACs. Of course, for complete understanding of concepts and student participation in the curriculum, all experiments should be performed whenever practical. Materials for the experiments are shown in Teacher Notes—Materials Needed.

LAB SAFETY
A few simple rules will guide your safe use of chemicals and equipment in a science laboratory.

1. Always wear safety goggles and lab apron. Surgical gloves are also helpful.
2. Wipe up all spills immediately with a wet sponge. Wash out the sponge with lots of water.
3. Wash off any chemicals from hands or other body parts with lots of water.
4. Handle all equipment and chemicals with care and caution.
5. Keep focused on the task at hand. Distractions lead to accidents.
6. Plan ahead. Read through each experiment before you start. Be sure to have plenty of room to work.
7. Carry out the experiments on a level, hard, non-porous table top. This makes cleanup easy.
8. Wash and clean up all equipment exposed to chemicals as soon as the activity is completed. Dirty equipment can mean danger.
9. Be sure to use a well ventilated room. Sometimes chemicals can have a very strong odor.
10. Have fun.

Science Projects List

Key

(1)	=	Those essential to perform for basic understanding of scientific principles.	S	=	Equipment needed for home school or Christian school lab.
(2)	=	Those which should be performed as time permits.	E	=	Explanation or demonstration by instructor may replace student or class lab work.
(3)	=	Those not essential for mastery of LIFEPACs.	H	=	Suitable for homework or for home school students. (No lab equipment needed.)

Science 1101

pp			
	8	(2)	S, H
	10	(2)	S, H
	11	(2)	S, H
	13	(2)	S, H
	18	(1)	S, H

Science 1102

pp			
	5	(1)	S, H
	12-15	(1)	S, H
	20	(2)	H
	29	(1)	H
	34	(1)	S

Science 1103

pp			
	12	(1)	S
	20	(1)	S
	47-49	(1)	S

Science 1104

pp			
	5	(1)	S
	6	(1)	S
	7	(2)	S
	23	(1)	S or H
	25	(1)	S

Science 1105

pp			
	30	(1)	S

Science 1106

pp			
	2	(1)	S
	3	(1)	S
	5	(1)	S
	6	(1)	S
	27	(1)	S
	30	(2)	S
	37	(1)	S

Science 1107

pp			
	18	(1)	S
	27	(1)	S
	34	(1)	S
	59	(1)	H

Science 1108-1110 none

Materials Needed for LIFEPAC
Required:
- metric rulers or meter sticks
- small beakers or glass jars
- 10-ml, 50-ml, and 100-ml graduated cylinders
- balance
- 125-ml and 250-ml Erlenmeyer flasks (two bottles, like catchup bottles, with lids can be used for Erlenmeyer flasks)
- candles (birthday and household will work)
- soda straws
- Limewater: To make limewater, secure a medium sized jar with tight-fitting lid. Add water (preferably distilled or purified water) until 2/3 full. Add a teaspoon of lime to the jar, replace the lid and shake Let the mixture set for 24 hours. The clear liquid on top is the limewater, so when used pour off the clear liquid and leave the solid in the jar. To replenish the limewater, just add more water, shake, and let stand. Lime can be purchased from a hardware or lumber supply store as lime or whitewash.

Additional Learning Activities
Section I Metric Units
none
Section II Instrumentation
1. Provide materials for students to measure using metric rulers, triple-beam balance, and graduated cylinders.
2. Measure distances and objects with friends. Average these measurements. Measure again those that vary greatly.
3. Make a 1,000 cm³ box of cardboard or wood with a friend.
4. Make a box that is 10 cm on each side. Compare this box with one of 1,000 cm³.
5. In a world almanac look up units of measurement. Determine the advantages of the metric system over others.
6. In a mathematics book find a list of metric prefixes and their decimal numerals. Make a chart.
7. Make a meter wheel from cardboard. Cut a piece of cardboard with a circumference of one meter. Make a line on the edge of the wheel. Use a nail for an axle and mount the wheel on a handle. Count revolutions to measure distance.
8. Check merchandise in the grocery store. List those that have metric units.
Section III Observation and Hypothesizing
1. Provide students with graphs to determine direct and inverse relationships. Any algebra book will have examples.

2. Visit a computer center and observe the plotter and the results on the screen or printer. If possible, read the program.
3. Graph the hourly temperature and humidity for your area as reported in the newspaper or as determined by your own instruments. Are these two factors independent of each other?

Section IV Scientific Notation

Section V Careers in Chemistry

1. Invite guest speakers to visit the class to talk about careers in chemistry.
2. Visit a site where chemistry is part of the operation. These range from water and sewer plants to smelters.
3. With a friend visit places listed in the telephone directory and ask several people how they use chemistry.
4. Talk to neighbors, friends, and students and determine the amount of chemistry they need to function at work or school.
5. Visit a police department and ask how they use chemistry.

Materials Needed for LIFEPAC

Required:
- flashlight battery with light bulb, socket, and wire
- samples of aluminum, zinc, carbon, iron, copper, and sulfur
- test tube with paradichlorobenzene (12 to 15 g per student)
- two 250-ml beakers
- ring stand with rings and heat source
- two thermometers
- egg-coloring tablet,
- safety goggles
- candle
- solder,
- 100-ml beaker with watch glass to fit
- hand lens
- white sand, salt, filter, paper, and funnel
- vegetable oil, vinegar, egg, salt, canned whipped topping (optional), canned shaving foam (optional), stirring rods, sugar, mustard, milk, homogenized, sour milk, 1-2-3 Jello (optional), blender, 150-ml beaker (or large baby food jar)
- grease pencil clean white sand, grape drink powder, 15 small baby-food jars, gauze, 100-ml graduated cylinder, 30-cm glass tubing, 1-hole stopper to fit tubing, short pipe or glass tube
- centrifuge: A centrifuge can be made by securely taping a 3-4 foot string on a test tube and rapidly swinging the test tube around the head. Tape the test tube to the string and put a cork stopper in the test tube before you start the swinging motion.

Suggested:
Curie, Eve. *Madame Curie*. New York: Pocket Books, Inc., no date
Jaffe, Bernard. *Crucibles: The Story of Chemistry from Ancient Alchemy to Nuclear Fission*. Magnolia, MA: Peter Smith Publisher, Inc., no date.

Additional Learning Activities

Section I Elements

1. Find samples of elements such as sulfur, carbon, lead, copper, manganese, and zinc. Have students classify them as metals or nonmetals by the properties they observe.
2. Visit a mine or refinery and write a report on the trip, giving information concerning the use of chemistry.
3. Explain why people before the year AD 1400 knew about the properties of iron, lead, sulfur, copper, and gold.

Section II Compounds

1. Purchase or make a set of atomic models from a science supply company and help the students assemble models of water, oxygen, carbon dioxide, and other simple molecules.
2. Visit a pharmacy and observe how medicines are compounded
3. Find the chemical formulas for quartz, feldspar, and other common minerals. Determine what, if any, commercial value each mineral has.

Section III Mixtures
1. Prepare a mixture of sodium nitrate and silicon dioxide. Have students examine the mixture with a magnifying glass or microscope.
2. Make a mixture of iodine crystals and alcohol. (Do not touch the crystals.) Before mixing, determine the mass of each. Is it possible to get the iodine crystals back again? (See the warning in the LIFEPAC.)
3. Find a piece of granite and examine it under a lens. Find the quartz and feldspar crystals. Look for other materials also.

Materials Needed for LIFEPAC

Required:
- plastic syringe (10 to 50 cc) with rubber stopper to fit top, mass hanger with mass pieces up to 3 kg, (can use 8 oz cans of food as weight)
- ring stand with platform ring
- 2 balloons, cloth measuring tape, thermometer
- cardboard (optional)
- balance, pH paper, 400-ml and 600-ml beaker, hot plate, chemicals (4.4 g $Cu(NO_3)_2$, (7 g powdered Zn, 30 ml 6M NaOH, 70 ml 3M H_2SO_4), 5 inch watch glass or glass square
- Recipes for making solutions:
  6M NaOH = dissolve 24.0 grams of solid NaOH in 100 ml of solution
  3M H_2SO_4 = slowly pour 16 ml of concentrated 18M H_2SO_4 into 90 ml of water. Slowly add enough water to make 100 ml of solution.

Suggested:
Frisch, O. R. *The Nature of Matter*. New York:
Frisch, O. R. *Working with Atoms*. New York:
Basic Books Inc 1965.
E. P. Dutton and Company, 1973.

Additional Learning Activities

Section I Kinetic Molecular Theory
1. In the back of a room, release the odors of orange, perfume, and ammonia, one at a time. Have fellow students spread throughout the room. Time the spread of each odor.
2. Measure out 5 ml of water into two identical beakers. Keep one at 85°C and the other at 95°C. Note the length of time it takes each sample to evaporate completely. Repeat three times and graph the data.

Section II Boyle's Law
1. Pump up a tire or ball using a hand pump. Explain why pumping becomes more difficult with time.
2. Talk to a diver or welder and learn why tanks must not be dropped or punctured.

Section III Charles' Law
1. Talk to a balloonist and learn why flights are not scheduled for hot days.
2. Talk to a tire expert and learn why tire pressures may have to be altered between summer and winter.
3. Many aerosol can labels indicate that the can should not be stored at temperatures greater than 120°F. Bring in such a label and determine the importance of the warning.

Section IV Combined Gas Law
none

Section V Moles
1. Find a copper, silver, or gold coin. Determine its mass and then mathematically calculate the number of atoms in that coin. Repeat for any other pure elements you can find.
2. Weigh out one mole of NaCl, $C_{11}H_{22}O_{11}$, H_2O, and C. Explain to several friends that each sample has the same number of molecules.

Materials Needed for LIFEPAC

Required:
- samples of pure elements, a chemistry handbook and tin-can lid with four indentations, reference textbook, LIFEPAC 1103 ring stand with ring and heat source, samples of iron, copper, magnesium, and lead
- two vinyl strips, two acetate strips, masking tape, two 40-cm pieces of nylon string
- metal Slinky®
- milk carton lids, water, heat source, nicrome wire with handle, hand spectroscope, solid compounds of copper, sodium, lithium, calcium, and potassium
- 20 note cards

Suggested:
Asimov, Isaac. *Inside the Atom*. New York: Abelard-Schuman, 1961.

Additional Learning Activities

Section I Contributors to a Concept
1. Talk to a scientist or doctor and write a report on current research problems in their field. Use the library for supplemental information.

Section II Modern Atomic Structure
1. Make a mobile of five models of atoms. The result should be scientifically accurate and artistic.

Section III Atomic Periodicity
1. Make a large periodic chart using samples or pictures whenever possible to represent the elements. Donate the project to a science teacher.

Section IV Nuclear Reactions
1. Arrange a formal debate on the topic "Resolved: The United States should build nuclear power plants wherever possible." Follow the rules of organized debate.

Materials Needed for LIFEPAC

Required:
- acetate strip and tissue paper, vinyl strip and woolen cloth
- slow stream of water
- styrofoam ball of at least 10 cm diameter, 8 nails of 4-5 cm length

Suggested:
Frisch, O. R. *The Nature of Matter*. New York: E. P. Dutton and Company, 1973.
Holliday, L. "Early Views on Forces Between Atoms," *Scientific American*, May 1970.

Additional Learning Activies

Section I Chemical Formulas
1. Make an interesting poster giving the formulas of all of the common items the group can find. Chemistry texts should be used to find formulas.

Section II Chemical Bonding
1. Write an explanation for why the rare gases of Column VIIIA do not have values for electronegativity.
2. Talk to an electrician and find out what materials are used in wires and insulators. Learn the safety rules for working with electricity.

Section III Molecular Shape and Electron Distribution
1. Find out how biologists use the word hybrid when discussing plants and animals.
2. Make models of three compounds using interesting and artistic materials. Ask for permission to have your models on display. Label the project.
3. Water is a polar molecule. Write a science fiction story about a day when water became a nonpolar molecule. Feel free to ask a chemist or a physicist for ideas.

Materials Needed for LIFEPAC:

Required:
- small test tubes,
  0.01 M solutions of NaCl,
  K_2CrO_4, $AgNO_3$, $FeSO_4$, $KMnO_4$,
  and NH_4NO_3, eye droppers
- concentrated HCl and acetic acid,
  HCl of 6 M, 1 M, 0.1 M
  acetic acid of 6 M, 1 M, chalk
- solid NaOH and NH_4OH, phenolphthalein
  solution, thermometers, forceps,
  test tubes with stoppers
- large jar, 20 square beads or
  blocks, 10 round beads or blocks
- Alka-Seltzer® tablets, baby food
  jars or beakers
- hydrogen peroxide; small pieces
  of liver, raw meat, or fresh
  pineapple; 100-ml graduated
  cylinder; test tubes with stoppers; and plastic tubing
- Recipe for solutions: Each is given in the LIFEPAC.

Suggested:
Asimov, Isaac. *Asimov on Chemistry*. Garden City, NY: Doubleday and Company, 1974.

Additional Learning Activities

Section I Chemical Reactions
1. Arrange a visit to a local medical laboratory. Have a registered medical technologist show the group the variety of instruments used to detect reactions and concentrations.

Section II Reaction Rate
1. Learn why milk and other dairy products have varying shelf lives depending on temperatures in the cooler or refrigerator.
2. Talk to a nurse and find out why high body temperatures are so dangerous.
3. Find out why only cooked pineapple can be used when making gelatin-based salads or desserts.

Section III Reaction Equilibriums
1. Write a paragraph telling why a heat source is used for so many chemical reactions in the laboratory.
2. Mix 50 ml of tap water with 50 grams of salt. Pour off the water into a clean beaker and let the solution evaporate. Make daily observations and explain the results.

Materials Needed for LIFEPAC

Required: Suggested:

- rock salt, rubbing alcohol, test tubes, glycerine, 2 baby food jars with lids, stirring rod
- water, hard tap water, softened water and rain or distilled water, non-detergent liquid soap, glass microscope slide, household chemicals such as $CaCl_2$, $NaCl$, NH_4OH, $Mg(OH)_2$, $Na_2B_4O_7$, Na_2CO_3, $FeCl_3$, KCl, K_2CO_3, hot plate, microscope
- distilled water, HCl O.1 M, 0.001 M, and 0.00001 M, chalk chips or limestone, 4 test tubes
- silver coil or tableware, sulfur from egg or match, hot plate, aluminum pan, baking soda, tarnished silver
- apple, 7 test tubes with stoppers, boiled and fresh tap water, Vitamin C tablets, fruit juice containing Vitamin C

Additional Learning Activities

Section I Solutions

1. Determine the molecular weights of at least seven items from your kitchen, medicine chest, or workshop.
2. Make a poster explaining the three main types of solutions. Use magazine pictures if possible.
3. Find a volunteer who is not studying chemistry. Teach your volunteer how to determine the gram formula weights of $NaCl$, H_2O, and $C_{11}H_{22}O_{11}$.
4. Test a penny for copper by placing it in ammonia. A blue coloration will develop when copper is present. Test other coins for copper after practicing with the penny.
5. Make a complete set of models to demonstrate: $2H_2 + O_2 \longrightarrow 2H_2O$. Use your models to explain to a fellow student the idea behind balancing an equation.

Section II Solubility Equilibriums

1. Place 50 ml of water into 3 identical jars with lids. Drop a sugar cube into one jar, an equal mass of granulated sugar into the second jar, and an equal mass of powdered sugar into the third jar. Keep track of how many shakes it takes to dissolve each of the three sugar samples. Repeat using three grades of salt.

Section III Acid-Base Equilibriums

1. Purchase phenaphthazine paper from a drug store and determine the pH of 20 items from your home or school.
2. Obtain a list of food recommended for ulcer patients. Test as many of these foods as possible with phenaphthazine paper. Write a statement about the pH of a typical ulcer patient's diet.
3. Find out why baking soda is sprinkled on acid spills in the laboratory.
4. Contact the local poison control center and learn the antidote for acid and base poisoning. Also learn why they do not recommend that a child who has swallowed an acid be given a base to drink even though the base would neutralize the acid in the child's stomach.

5. Talk to a doctor, nurse, or coach and learn about the buffering system in the blood.
6. Why would a very precise chemist never ask for "the salt" at the dinner table? Write a one-paragraph answer.

Section IV Redox Equilibriums

1. Make flashcards of the anions in the LIFEPAC and memorize them.
2. Some chemical labels state that the contents are strong oxidizing agents. What does this warning mean and what precautions should be taken? Consult the poison control center for recommendations.

Materials Needed for LIFEPAC
> Required:
> none

Suggested:

Asimov, Isaac. *The World of Carbon.* New York: AbelardSchuman, 1958.

Lambert, J. R. "The Shapes of Organic Molecules," *Scientific American*, January 1970.

Lessing, L. P. "Coal," *Scientific American*, July 1955.

Mills, G. A. "Ubiquitous Hydrocarbons," *Chemistry*, February 1971.

Additional Learning Activities

Section I Carbon Compounds

1. List twenty organic and twenty inorganic items used in and around your home or school.
2. Write a report on the La Brea tar pits of (Los Angeles) Southern California.

Section II Carbon Atoms

1. Make a model of the carbon atom that shows clearly the possibility of a +4 valence.
2. Make a poster showing the three forms of carbon. The presentation should be scientific but useful to a student who has not had chemistry. Use samples of carbon and graphite and a picture of a diamond.
3. Write a report on the discovery and development of rubber vulcanization. Include a sketch of the vulcanized molecule.

Section III Hydrogen and Carbon

1. Find and draw the structure of the gasoline additive tetraethyl lead.
2. Investigate polyethylene plastic and write a report on its discovery, naming, and important uses.
3. Talk to a welder and learn about the special uses and safety precautions of acetylene welding.
4. List thirty plastic items used in your home or school.
5. Check clothing labels and clothing catalogs for the names of synthetic fibers. Make a list of the advantages and disadvantages of synthetic fibers and the fabrics they produce.

Materials Needed for LIFEPAC
Required:
none

Suggested:
Cook, J. G. *The Miracle of Plastics*. New York: 1964.The Dial Press,
Morton, M. "Teflon-From Nonstick Frying Pans to Space Vehicles," *Chemistry*, June 1965.

Additional Learning Activities
Section I Hydrocarbon Chemistry
1. Write a report on the use of freon in aerosol cans and auto air conditioning systems and its suspected damage to the ozone layer.
2. Write a report on Teflon and other coatings.
3. Chlorinated benzene derivatives are suspected to have caused great damage to wildlife. Write a report on the environmental damage of DDT to the bird population and why the use of DDT is now limited.

Section II Oxygen Functional Groups
1. An organic acid (fat) plus sodium hydroxide (NaOH) yields soap plus water. Read old books or talk to persons who know how to make soap. Under careful supervision try making a small bar of soap.
2. Look up the formula for ethylene glycol and describe the properties that make it a valuable economic product.
3. Write a report on the manufacture of nitroglycerine and its use in explosions and medicine.
4. Talk to a nurse and learn about the production of acetone in diabetic persons.
5. Find a sun tan preparation label that lists dihydroxyacetone and draw the formula.
6. Citric acid is a common addition to fruit juice drinks and soft drinks. Find the formula for citric acid and the reason for its presence in so many beverages.

Section III Nitrogen Functional Groups
1. Most amines have an unpleasant odor, but triethanolamine is used in many health and beauty aids for both men and women. Find a preparation that lists this amine as an ingredient and then draw its structure.
2. Read the story of Wallace Carothers of DuPont and his discovery of nylon.
3. Protein is an important aspect of proper nutrition that is commonly lacking in the diets of the poor. Make a list of inexpensive vegetable sources of protein.

Materials Needed for LIFEPAC
Required: Suggested:
none   none

Additional Learning Activities
Section I Characteristics of Atoms and Molecules
1. Show a movie or filmstrip on the use and advantages of the metric system. Your public library will probably have some you can check out.
2. Lead a class discussion on why it is important that all scientists use the metric system. Is the United States making a good decision to change over to metrics?
3. With a classmate make a large poster showing the classification of matter. Hang the poster in your classroom.
4. With a classmate plan and perform an experiment to show whether hot water or cold water weighs more. Explain your results.
5. Select a topic from Section I of LIFEPAC 1110. Research it more fully in the library and write a three- to five page paper on it. Turn your research paper in to your teacher.
6. Make a poster or construct models of several atoms. Styrofoam balls work well for atomic models.

Section II Chemical Systems
1. Discuss the role of catalysts in chemical reactions. Demonstrate the process of titration to your class.
2. Visit a professional or local college chemistry lab. If you set up a tour with several friends ahead of time, you will probably be able to see several experiments taking place.
3. With a classmate demonstrate how acids, bases, and salts react. Drop a dull copper penny into a dish of vinegar. Leave it a few seconds and then describe what happened. Remove the penny and add a teaspoon of salt to the vinegar. Again place the penny in the solution. What happens to the color of the penny? How do you know whether a chemical change has taken place?
4. Select a topic from Section II of LIFEPAC 1110. Research your topic, and prepare a three- to five-page report. Turn your paper in to your teacher.
5. Make a list of different household or common laboratory chemicals that need special care to prevent undesirable chemical changes. Tell how such changes can be avoided. (Example: Light sensitive chemicals are stored in dark bottles.)

Section III Organic Chemistry
1. Discuss the difference between organic chemistry and inorganic chemistry with your class.
2. On the blackboard demonstrate the difference between substitution reactions and addition reactions by writing out several equations of each type as examples.
3. With a classmate make a poster that shows the organization of the elements in several hydrocarbon molecules. Display your poster in your classroom.
4. With a classmate visit with someone in a profession who needed a background in organic chemistry. Ask about their work and report your findings to your class.

5. Write a two- to three-page report on alcohols. Use research books in the library to help you.
6. Select a topic from Section III of LIFEPAC 1110. Do further research on your topic and make an oral report to your class on what you learned.

Additional Activity

Select a topic from the 1100 LIFEPAC series. Research your topic fully. Your final project should include a five-page written report, a visual project such as a poster or class demonstration, and an oral report to share what you learned with your class. Your written report should contain a bibliography. Check with your teacher to approve your topic and to determine a due date before you begin.

TESTS

Reproducible Tests
for use with the Science 1100
Teacher's Guide

Name _____

Match these items (each answer, 2 points).

1. _____ $xy = k$ a. $\frac{1}{100}$

2. _____ primary unit of mass   b. direct relationship

3. _____ ±   c. unit of distance

4. _____ qualitative   d. milliliter

5. _____ centi   e. $\frac{1}{1000}$ kg

6. _____ theory   f. explanation accepted without
                                            question

7. _____ mm
                                        g. inverse relationship

8. _____ ml
                                        h. accuracy

9. _____ straight-line graph
                                        i. well accepted explanation

10. _____ g
                                        j. type of observation

                                        k. kilogram

Write the letter for the correct answer on each line (each answer, 2 points).

11. The best way to write 960,200 in scientific notation is _____.

   a. $9.60200 \cdot 10^5$ c. $9.6 \cdot 10^4$
   b. $9.602 \cdot 10^5$ d. $9,602 \cdot 10^2$

12. The accuracy of an instrument is the _____ of the instrument.

   a. quality   c. precision
   b. cost   d. size

13. The number $6.02 \cdot 10^{-1}$ can be written as _____.

   a. 0.0602   c. 0.0062
   b. 0.602   d. 6.02

14. Observations describing the color of a substance are most likely _____.

   a. quantitative   c. qualitative
   b. too general   d. inaccurate

15. The instrument that could best be used to measure mass is a _____.

   a. balance   c. pipette
   b. graduated cylinder   d. ruler

45

16. Which graph best illustrates an $\frac{y}{x} = k$ relationship? _____

    a. [graph] b. [graph] c. [graph] d. [graph]

17. The instrument you would use for the most accurate volume measurement is _____.

    a. a burette   c. a graduated cylinder
    b. an Erlenmeyer flask   d. a beaker

18. The number, 16,694,000, has _____ significant numbers.

    a. 5   c. 3
    b. 8   d. 2

19. Which of the following is a unit of volume:

    a. mg   b. km   c. g   d. ml

20. The number, 9,876,444,001, has _____ significant numbers.

    a. 1   c. 5
    b. 7   d. 10

Complete these activities (each answer, 3 points).

21. List three careers in chemistry you have studied.

    a. _____

    b. _____

    c. _____

22. The equation $\frac{y}{x} = k$ is a(n) _____ relationship.

23. Write 0.016648 in scientific notation. _____

24. Express 0.000319001 to 3 significant numbers. _____

25. The accuracy value for a 10-ml graduated cylinder is _____.

26. Secure three unknowns from your teacher. Perform the appropriate measurements to determine the mass, length, and volume of the three quantities.

    a. mass _____   b. mass _____   c. mass _____

       volume _____   volume _____   volume _____

       length _____   length _____   length _____

27. Express $(6.994 \cdot 10^1) \div (2.00 \cdot 10^1)$ in scientific notation.

_____

28. $(9.094)(19.20) =$ _____ (express in scientific notation).

Complete this activity (this answer, 5 points).

29. Develop a set of data and plot the data for an equation showing an inverse relationship when k = 9.

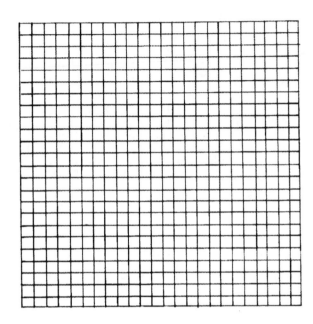

	x	y	k
a.			9
b.			9
c.			9
d.			9
e.			9

$\boxed{\begin{array}{l} 64 \\ \quad 81 \end{array}}$

Date _____

Score _____

Name _____

Figure 16. Periodic Table of the Elements

Answer *true* or *false* (each answer, 1 point).

1. _____ Cu is an element.

2. _____ C_6H_6 is an inorganic compound.

3. _____ Iced tea is an example of a heterogeneous mixture.

4. _____ Not all matter occupies space.

5. _____ Compounds can never be pure substances.

6. _____ The word *science* comes from the Latin word *scio*.

7. _____ Melting an ice cube releases energy.

8. _____ Potential energy means stored energy.

9. _____ A phase change always requires added energy.

10. _____ Alexandria was the center of alchemy.

Complete these activities (each answer, 2 points).

11. Indicate whether each of the following events is a *physical, phase,* or *chemical* change.

    a. _____ Evaporating gasoline

    b. _____ Broken leg

    c. _____ Painting a car

    d. _____ Paint fading colors

    e. _____ Cloud formation

    f. _____ Digestion of food

48

12. Indicate whether each of the following items is an *inorganic* or *organic* compound.

a. _____ $CaCl_2$ d. _____ NO_2

b. _____ $C_{12}H_{26}$ e. _____ $C_6H_4Cl_2$

c. _____ $C_8H_{20}Pb$ f. _____ $CuCO_3$

13. Indicate whether each of the following items is a *pure substance* or a *mixture*.

a. _____ whipped cream   d. _____ brass

b. _____ table salt   e. _____ distilled water

c. _____ concrete   f. _____ wood

14. Indicate whether each of the following items is an *element* or *compound*.

a. _____ $C_{12}H_{26}$ d. _____ $CaCl_2$

b. _____ Na   e. _____ H_2O

c. _____ N   f. _____ Ca

Complete these statements (each answer, 3 points).

Questions 15 through 18 pertain to the following graph. A gas was cooled by dry ice. The temperature of the sample confined in a test tube was noted every 30 seconds.

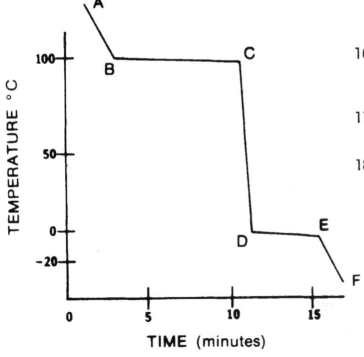

15. The portion of the graph between a. _____ and b. _____ represents the substance being cooled as a liquid.

16. The portion between a. _____ and b. _____ represents the substance being cooled as a gas.

17. A molecule at point a. _____ has the least amount of energy.

18. Between a. _____ and b. _____ the substance exists both as a solid and a liquid.

49

Match these items (each answer, 2 points).

19. _____ hydrogen

20. _____ copper

21. _____ nitrogen

22. _____ iron

23. _____ sulfur

a. Co

b. Cu

c. H

d. N

e. Fe

f. S

Complete these activities (each answer, 5 points).

24. Describe two of the major events in the history of chemistry up to
1750 that have contributed to our knowledge today.

_____

_____

_____

_____

_____

25. Describe the differences between heterogeneous and homogeneous mixtures
and give two examples of each, explaining how and why they fit into the
class you say they do.

_____

_____

_____

_____

_____

_____

_____

_____

80 / 99

Date _____

Score _____

Name _____

Match these items (each answer, 2 points).

1. _____ diffusion

2. _____ Boyle's Law

3. _____ Kelvin

4. _____ combined gas law

5. _____ temperature

6. _____ Avogadro's Hypothesis

7. _____ Charles' Law

8. _____ vapor pressure

9. _____ mole

10. _____ reactants

a. molecules escaping from liquid phase into gaseous phase

b. relates temperature and volume

c. solid state

d. relates temperature, volume, and pressure

e. equal volumes of gas have equal number of molecules under the same conditions

f. one gram-formula-weight

g. starting materials

h. intermingling of atoms from one substance into another

i. relates pressure and volume

j. absolute temperature scale

k. a measure of average kinetic energy

Write the letter for the correct answer on each line (each answer, 2 points).

11. If the pressure on a balloon is increased from 1 atm to 6 atm while the temperature is held constant, the new volume of a 1-liter balloon will be _____ liters.

   a. .6   c. .167
   b. 6   d. 1.67

12. Molecules vibrate around fixed points in _____.

   a. reactions   c. liquids
   b. gases   d. solids

13. If pressure is held constant, volume varies directly with _____.

   a. ^{0}K   c. ^{0}F
   b. ^{0}C   d. ^{0}A

14. One mole of a gas contains _____.

   a. 273 molecules   c. $273 \cdot 10^{-23}$ molecules
   b. 760 molecules   d. $6.02 \cdot 10^{23}$ molecules

15. Continually moving air particles cause _____.

   a. Boyle's Law   c. air pressure
   b. Charles' Law   d. vapor pressure

16. If pressure is held constant while the temperature is increased from 0°C to 273°C, 1 liter of gas would _____.

    a. increase to 2 liters
    b. decrease to zero liters
    c. increase to 273 liters
    d. decrease to 0.5 liters

17. What pressure is necessary to increase the volume of a 3-liter balloon at 1 atm to 6 liters if temperature is held constant? _____

    a. 3 atm
    b. .5 atm
    c. 6 atm
    d. 2 atm

18. A 100-cm³ weather balloon is launched at 20°C and 750 mm Hg. The volume of the balloon when it reaches an altitude where the temperature is 0°C and the pressure is 500 mm will be _____.

    a. $\dfrac{(100)(20)(500)}{(273)(750)}$

    b. $\dfrac{100(293)(750)}{(273)(500)}$

    c. $\dfrac{(100)(0)(750)}{(20)(500)}$

    d. $\dfrac{(100)(273)(750)}{(293)(500)}$

Complete these activities (each lettered item, 3 points).

Determine the gram-formula-weights of the following compounds.

19. a. H_2O _____

    b. $C_{11}H_{22}O_{11}$ _____

    c. $Cu(NO_3)_2$ _____

    d. $NaOH$ _____

    e. $AgNO_3$ _____

Balance these equations.

20. Zn + _____ $HCl \longrightarrow ZnCl_2$ + H_2

21. Cu + a. _____ $HNO_3 \longrightarrow Cu(NO_3)_2$ + b. _____ NO_2 +

    c. _____ H_2O

22. a. _____ Na + b. _____ $H_2O \longrightarrow$ c. _____ $NaOH$ + H_2

Calculate the answers to the following problems. Use the following equation as the basis of your calculations (each answer, 5 points).

$$2PbO_2 \longrightarrow 2PbO + O_2$$

23. How many liters of oxygen are formed if 478 g of PbO_2 are reacted?

24. How many grams of PbO are formed if 478 g of PbO_2 are reacted?

66	
	82

Date _____

Score _____

Name _____

Match these items (each answer, 2 points).

1. _____ Democritus

2. _____ Rutherford

3. _____ Thomson

4. _____ Chadwick

5. _____ Dalton

6. _____ Schrodinger

7. _____ Curie

8. _____ Bohr

9. _____ Mendeleev

10. _____ Geiger

a. originated modern atomic theory

b. predicted positron

c. discovered radium

d. developed nuclear model of atom

e. discovered acetate

f. matter consists of small particles

g. quantum theory

h. common scintillation counter named for him

i. discovered neutrons

j. proved existence of electron

k. arranged first periodic table of elements

Write the letter for the correct answer on each line (each answer, 2 points).

11. The protons and neutrons of an atom make up the _____.

a. sublevel
b. orbital
c. quantum
d. nucleus

12. An element differing in the number of neutrons only is _____.

a. radioactive
b. an isotope
c. a compound
d. an orbital

13. The number of protons gives an element its _____.

a. half life
b. orbital
c. atomic number
d. symbol

14. The number of electrons in a neutral atom is the same as the number of _____.

a. protons
b. neutrons
c. isotopes
d. orbitals

15. The number of protons plus neutrons is the _____ number.

a. mass
b. orbital
c. atomic
d. isotope

16. Electrons can occupy only _____ .

    a. s orbitals
    b. p sublevels
    c. a particular energy level
    d. d sublevels

17. The region of space where an electron is most probably located is the _____ .

    a. nucleus
    b. isotope
    c. quantum
    d. orbital

18. In chemistry, s, p, d, and f represent _____ .

    a. spectra
    b. sublevels
    c. ions
    d. quanta

19. The nuclear mass that is converted into binding energy is _____ .

    a. fusion
    b. fission
    c. mass defect
    d. fallout

20. Our sun is an example of _____ .

    a. decay chain
    b. fision
    c. disintegration
    d. fusion

Complete these nuclear equations (each answer, 3 points).

21. $^{234}_{92}U \longrightarrow\, ^{230}_{90}Th\ +$ _____

22. $^{252}_{98}Cf \longrightarrow\, ^{4}_{2}He\ +$ _____

Write the orbital representation for each of the following elements using the $1s^2 2s^2 2p^6$, etc. format (each answer, 3 points).

23. chlorine _____

24. sodium _____

25. beryllium _____

Name the element that is represented by the following orbital representations (each answer, 3 points).

26. $1s^2 2s^2 2p^6 3s^2 3p^6 4s^2$ _____

27. $1s^2 2s^2 2p^6 3s^2 3p^6$ _____

28. $1s^2 2s^2 2p^6$ _____

29. $1s^2 2s^2 2p^6 3s^2 3p^6 4s^2 3d^{10} 4p^6 5s^2 4d^9$ _____

30. $1s^2 2s^2 2p^6 3s^2 3p^3$ _____

56 / 70

Date _____

Score _____

Name _____

Match these items (each answer, 2 points).

1. _____ HCl   a. plane triangular

2. _____ CH_2Br_2 b. pyramidal

3. _____ $AlCl_3$ c. bent

4. _____ H_2O d. linear

5. _____ PCl_3 e. tetrahedral

                                 f. oval

Write the letter for the correct answer on each line (each answer, 2 points).

6. The formula for a compound of hydrogen and carbon would be _____.

   a. CH_5 c. CH_3
   b. CH d. CH_4

7. The formula for a compound of beryllium and fluorine would be _____.

   a. BeF c. BeF_2
   b. Be_2F d. Be_2F_3

8. The formula for a compound of sodium and bromine would be _____.

   a. Na_2Br c. $NaBr_2$
   b. Na_3Br_2 d. $NaBr$

9. The formula for a compound of magnesium and oxygen would be _____.

   a. MgO c. MgO_2
   b. Mg_2O d. Mg_2O_3

10. The formula for a compound of aluminum and iodine would be _____.

    a. AlI_3 c. Al_3I
    b. AlI d. AlI_2

11. The electron attracting ability of an atom is its _____.

    a. bonding rate   c. ionizing
    b. electronegativity   d. hybridization

12. The element with the greatest electronegativity is _____.

    a. sodium   c. fluorine
    b. carbon   d. hydrogen

57

13. A mixture of different types of orbitals is called _____.

    a. hybrid bond   c. geometric bond
    b. sublevel   d. quantum level

14. The elements with the lowest electronegativity would be from column _____.

    a. IA   c. VIIA
    b. VIA   d. IIIA

15. The type of bond characterized by the mobility of electrons is _____ bond.

    a. ionic   c. metallic
    b. covalent   d. hybrid

Make the following calculations (each answer, 3 points).

Use the Periodic Table of the Elements to determine the per cent ionic character of the bond in each of the following compounds.

16. LiCl   _____

17. NO_2 _____

18. HCl   _____

19. $AlBr_3$ _____

20. BeO   _____

Write *ionic*, *metallic*, or *covalent* after each of the following substances (each answer, 2 points).

21. NaCl   _____

22. iron pipe   _____

23. CO_2 _____

24. $MgBr_2$ _____

25. SO_2 _____

26. gold coin   _____

Write *polar* or *nonpolar* after each of the following molecules (each answer, 2 points).

27. Cl_2 _____

28. NaBr _____

29. $AlCl_3$ _____

30. H_2O _____

52	
	65

Date _____

Score _____

Name _____

Match these items (each answer, 2 points).

1. _____ precipitate

2. _____ endothermic

3. _____ Law of Conservation of Energy

4. _____ entropy

5. _____ catalyst

6. _____ rate

7. _____ equilibrium

8. _____ activation energy

9. _____ exothermic

10. _____ heat of reaction

a. the amount of energy in a closed system does not change

b. energy necessary for a reaction to begin

c. change per unit of time

d. energy gained

e. ΔH

f. balance between opposing events

g. randomness

h. energy lost

i. a solid formed during a reaction

j. activation complex

k. changes rate of reaction without being changed

Complete these statements (each answer, 2 points).

11. When acid is dropped on a piece of chalk, a reaction takes place. This reaction is detected by noting _____ .

12. Energy tied up in a chemical system is called _____ .

13. A reaction with a **negative** ΔH indicates that energy is being

_____ .

14. When two opposing forces are in balance, the system is in _____

_____ .

15. The equilibrium of a reaction is affected by a. _____ ,

b. _____ , and c. _____ .

16. A system is in equilibrium if for every molecule that leaves the surface of a liquid another molecule _____ .

17. Enzymes, powdered metals, and rough surfaces are examples of

_____ .

18. A gas used for cooking stoves would have to have what sign in front of ΔH? _____

60

Complete these items (each answer, 5 points).

19. Calculate the ΔH for the reaction $2H_2 + O_2 \longrightarrow 2H_2O$

$$H-H = 104 \qquad\qquad H-O = 111$$

$$O-O = 119$$

20. Draw and label an enthalpy diagram for the following reaction.

$$CH_4 + 2O_2 \longrightarrow CO_2 + 2H_2O \qquad\qquad ΔH = -115 \text{ kcal}$$

Label: a. reactants
        b. products
        c. ΔH

21. Label the following energy diagram.

    a. _____

    b. _____

    c. _____

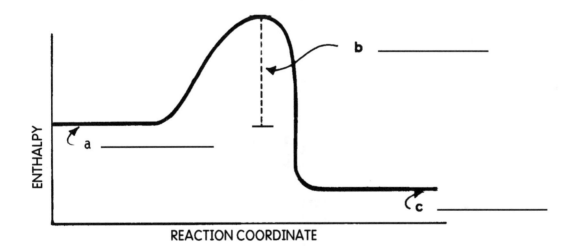

69 / 86

Date _____

Score _____

Science 1107 Alternate Test

Name _____

Match these items (each answer, 2 points).

1. _____ increases reaction rate

2. _____ heterogeneous solution

3. _____ neutral

4. _____ acid

5. _____ ion

6. _____ reduction

7. _____ solute

8. _____ anion

9. _____ base

10. _____ oxidation

a. electrons not equal to protons

b. yields H_3O^+ in water

c. substance that is dissolving

d. $OH^- = H^+$

e. pulverize, heat, stir

f. composed of various materials

g. electrons added

h. positive ion

i. electrons are donated

j. yields OH^- in water

k. negative ion

Write the letter for the correct answer on each line (each answer, 2 points).

11. The gram-formula-weight of $NaHCO_3$ is _____.
    (Na = 23, O = 16, C = 12, H = 1)

    a. 52   c. 84
    b. 51   d. 61

12. The K_{eq} for $aA + bB \rightleftharpoons cC + dD$ is _____.

    a. $\dfrac{[C]^d[D]^c}{[A]^b[B]^a}$

    b. $\dfrac{[C]^c[D]^d}{[A]^a[B]^b}$

    c. $\dfrac{[c]^C[d]^D}{[a]^A[b]^B}$

    d. $\dfrac{[A]^a[D]^d}{[B]^b[C]^c}$

13. The concentration of the H^+ ion is expressed by _____.

    a. OH   c. pH
    b. log   d. ΔH

62

14. The product of a neutralization reaction is _____ .

   a. a log   c. an acid
   b. a base   d. a salt

15. How many grams are in 2 M of NaCl? _____

   a. 23 g   c. 58.4 g
   b. 35.4 g   d. 116.8 g

16. $S^{-2} \longrightarrow S^{+4} + 6\ e^-$ is an example of _____ .

   a. equilibrium   c. a half-reaction
   b. molarity   d. neutralization

17. Balance this equation.

   $2KMnO_4 + 5H_2S +$ _____ $HCl \longrightarrow 2KCl + 2MnCl_2 +$ _____ $H_2O + 5S$

   a. 2, 4   c. 3, 4
   b. 6, 8   d. 2, 5

Balance these equations (each answer, 2 points).

18. a._____ HCl + b._____ $Zn \longrightarrow ZnCl_2$ + c._____ H_2

19. a._____ $Pb(NO_3)_2$ + b._____ $NaI \longrightarrow PbI_2$ + c._____ $NaNO_3$

Do this calculation (each answer, 5 points).

20. 10 ml of 1.0 M $AgNO_3$ is diluted to 1 liter with tap water. The Cl^- concentration of tap water is $1 \cdot 10^{-5}$ M.

   a. What is the concentration of Ag^+ in the diluted solution?

   b. If the K_{sp} of AgCl is $1.7 \cdot 10^{-10}$ will a precipitate form?

   c. Show proof of the answer.

<table>
<tr><td>48</td></tr>
<tr><td>61</td></tr>
</table>

Date _____

Score _____

Science 1108 Alternate Test

Name _____

Match these items (each answer, 2 points).

1. _____ organic chemistry

2. _____ C_2H_4

3. _____ covalent bond

4. _____ C_2H_2

5. _____ benzene

6. _____ tetrahedron

7. _____ saturated

8. _____ C_6H_{14}

9. _____ C_2H_6

10. _____ unsaturated

a. shape of carbon compounds

b. metal carbonate

c. ethane

d. C_6H_6

e. carbon compounds with only single bonds

f. ethyne

g. hexane

h. study of carbon compounds

i. ethylene

j. contains double or triple bond

k. electrons shared

Complete these statements (each answer, 3 points).

11. The three major sources of organic compounds are a. _____,

b. _____ , and c. _____ .

12. The three forms of carbon are a. _____, b. _____,

and c. _____ .

13. What is the electronic configuration of carbon using the $1s^2$ configuration?

_____

Balance these equations (each lettered answer, 2 points).

14. C_2H_8 + a. _____ $O_2 \longrightarrow$ b. _____ CO_2 + c. _____ H_2O

15. $2C_2H_6$ + a. _____ $O_2 \longrightarrow$ b. _____ CO_2 + c. _____ H_2O

16. C_2H_4 + a. _____ $O_2 \longrightarrow$ b. _____ CO_2 + c. _____ H_2O

Write the general formula for each of the following hydrocarbons (each answer, 5 points).

17. alkyne   _____

18. alkene   _____

19. alkane   _____

Write *organic* or *inorganic* after each of the following items (each answer, 2 points).

20. CO_2 _____

21. $C_{11}H_{22}O_{11}$ _____

22. C_2H_6 _____

23. $NaHCO_3$ _____

24. coal   _____

$\dfrac{67}{84}$

Date _____

Score _____

Name _____

Match these items (each answer, 2 points).

1. _____ amino acid

2. _____ saturated halide

3. _____ paradichlorobenzene

4. _____ ethyl alcohol

5. _____ ester

6. _____ acetone

7. _____ formaldehyde

8. _____ ethyl amine

9. _____ formic acid

10. _____ peptide linkage

a. 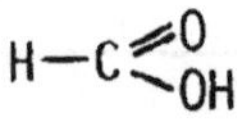 $H-C{\Large\diagdown}{\substack{\displaystyle O \\ OH}}$

b. 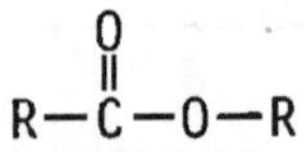 $R-\overset{\displaystyle O}{\overset{\|}{C}}-O-R$

c. C_2H_5OH

d. 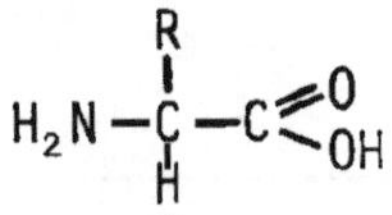 $H_2N-\overset{\displaystyle R}{\underset{\displaystyle H}{\overset{|}{\underset{|}{C}}}}-C{\Large\diagdown}{\substack{\displaystyle O \\ OH}}$

e. 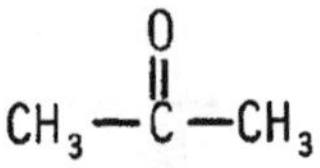 $CH_3-\overset{\displaystyle O}{\overset{\|}{C}}-CH_3$

f. $R-C-R$

g. 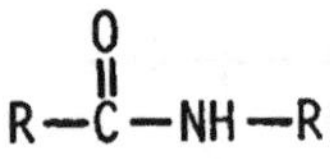 $R-\overset{\displaystyle O}{\overset{\|}{C}}-NH-R$

h.  (benzene ring with Cl at top and Cl at bottom)

i. $C_2H_5-NH_2$

j. CH_2O

k. 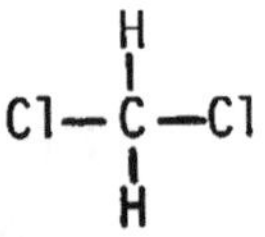 $Cl-\overset{\displaystyle H}{\underset{\displaystyle H}{\overset{|}{\underset{|}{C}}}}-Cl$

Complete these activities (each answer, 5 points).

11. Write and balance the equation for the reaction between methane and chlorine gas.

12. Write and balance the equation for the reaction between ethylene and fluorine gas.

Balance these equations (each answer, 2 points).

13. $2CH_3CHO + a.\underline{\hphantom{xxx}} O_2 \longrightarrow b.\underline{\hphantom{xxx}} CO_2 + c.\underline{\hphantom{xxx}} H_2O$

14. $C_6H_6 + \underline{\hphantom{xxxxx}} Br_2 \longrightarrow C_6H_6Br_6$

15. $C_2H_5OH + a.\underline{\hphantom{xxx}} O_2 \longrightarrow b.\underline{\hphantom{xxx}} CO_2 + c.\underline{\hphantom{xxx}} H_2O$

Match these items (each answer, 2 points).

16. _____ $CHCl_3$ a. vinegar

17. _____ formaldehyde   b. soap

18. _____ paradichlorobenzene   c. solvent for grease and oil

19. _____ enzyme   d. chain of amino acids

20. _____ isopropyl alcohol   e. nylon

21. _____ ester   f. mothballs

22. _____ polymeric amide   g. organic catalyst

23. _____ acetic acid   h. chloroform

24. _____ polypeptide   i. fruit flavors

25. _____ acetone   j. preservative and disinfectant

                                                     k. rubbing alcohol

51 / 64

Date _____

Score _____

Name _____

Answer *true* or *false* (each answer, 1 point).

1. _____ Color change is a good way to detect a chemical reaction.

2. _____ An equilibrium is not changed by a change in pressure.

3. _____ A + ΔH means that energy is released from a reaction.

4. _____ Enthalpy is the energy in chemicals holding them together.

5. _____ The reaction $P_4 + 5O_2 \rightleftharpoons P_4O_{10} + 712$ kcal is exothermic.

6. _____ An equilibrium is dynamic.

7. _____ Molarity is expressed in moles per liter,   [   ].

8. _____ When a precipitate forms, the reaction increases entropy.

9. _____ *Entropy* means *randomness*, or *disorder* in a system.

10. _____ The ΔH of a reaction is its heat of reaction.

11. _____ The gram has the symbol G.

12. _____ The scientific notation for 6,002. is $6.002 \cdot 10^{-3}$.

13. _____ A mole is equal to one g.f.w.

14. _____ All atoms above a temperature of $0°K$ are in motion.

15. _____ A theory that is accepted as true is a law.

Match these items (each answer, 2 points).

16. _____ Ca

17. _____ C_nH_{2n}

18. _____ $R-\overset{\overset{\displaystyle O}{\|}}{C}-O-R$

19. _____ reaction of C_2H_6

20. _____ functional element of amines

21. _____ air

22. _____ R-OH

23. _____ CH_4

24. _____ reactions of alkynes

25. _____ functional element of ketones

a. alkene

b. alkane

c. alcohol

d. ester

e. addition

f. substitution

g. nitrogen

h. oxygen

i. element

j. acid

k. mixture

Write the letter for the correct answer on each line (each answer, 2 points).

26. An inert gas has a _____ electron configuration.

   a. $1s^2 2s^2 2p^6$
   b. $2s^2 2p^2$
   c. $1s^2 2s^2 2p^6 3s^2$
   d. $1s^2 2s^2$

27. An element with ionization energies $E_1 = 110$, $E_2 = 146$, $E_3 = 984$, and $E_4 = 1,136$, has _____ valence electrons.

   a. 1
   b. 2
   c. 3
   d. 4

28. Ionization energy _____.

   a. is high for metals
   b. shows little relationship to the size of the atom
   c. shows a general increase vertically with increasing atomic number
   d. shows a decrease as the atomic number within a group increases

29. The most vigorous chemical reaction would likely come between _____.

   a. Fr and F
   b. Ca and F
   c. Na and F
   d. Ba and F

69

30. A covalent bond is formed by _____.

    a. gaining or losing two or more electrons by an atom
    b. sharing two electrons by two atoms
    c. sharing of an electron by two atoms
    d. loss of an electron by one atom to another

31. The bond between F and Cl would be _____.

    a. ionic   c. metallic
    b. pure covalent   d. polar covalent

32. The substance which would be the poorest conductor of electricity at room temperature is _____.

    a. Al   c. Co
    b. Au   d. S

33. The molecule most likely to be nonpolar is _____.

    a. I — Br   b.   S—F   c.   P   d.   Cl
                   /   / | \ |
                  F   F | F   B
                                    F   /   \
                                             Cl   Cl

34. A balloon with 20 ml of gas in it is put in a hot place and changes from 10° to 100°C. The pressure is increased by ten times its original. The best expression for the new volume is _____.

    a. $\dfrac{20 \times 373 \times 1}{283 \times 10}$ c. $\dfrac{20 \times 283 \times 1}{273 \times 10}$

    b. $\dfrac{20 \times 10 \times 1}{100 \times 10}$ d. $\dfrac{20 \times 373 \times 10}{283 \times 1}$

Date _____

Score _____

ANSWER KEYS

NOTE: Data tables can be found throughout the curriculum. They should be available to the student (where appropriate) anytime they are answering problems in section exercises, Self Tests, or LIFEPAC Tests.

1.1   Reports will vary.

1.2   kilometer:
      a.   0.1
      b.   0.0012
      c.   0.000001
      d.   0.063
      e.   0.0001263
      f.   0.0315
      h.   0.0000192
      i.   0.00684
      j.   0.0000093
      l.   0.0001516
      m.   0.000000031
      n.   0.1234
      p.   0.00366
      meter:
      b.   1.2
      c.   0.001
      e.   0.1263
      g.   536
      h.   0.0192
      j.   0.0093
      k.   61,390
      m.   0.000031
      n.   123.4
      o.   0.00036
      p.   3.66
      centimeter:
      a.   10,000
      d.   6,300
      e.   12.63
      f.   3,150
      g.   53,600
      i.   684
      j.   0.93
      k.   6,139,000
      l.   15.16
      n.   12,340
      o.   0.036
      p.   366
      millimeter:
      a.   100,000
      b.   1,200
      c.   1
      d.   63,000
      f.   31,500
      g.   536,000
      h.   19.2
      i.   6,840
      k.   61,390,000
      l.   151.6
      m.   0.031
      o.   0.36

1.3 cm^3:
      b.   2,100
      c.   1.05
      d.   941
      e.   100.5
      f. 10,300
      g.   0.025
      h. 22,400
      i.   12.86
      j.   321
      k.   22.4
      l   25
      ml:
      b.   2,100
      c.   1.05
      e.   100.5
      h. 22,400
      j.   321
      l.   25
      L:
      d.   0.941
      f.   10.30
      g.   0.000025
      i.   0.01286
      k.   0.0224

1.4   kg:
      a.   0.1
      b.   0.00000134
      c.   0.00001011
      e.   0.0854
      f.   0.0000379
      g.   0.01084
      h.   0.00905
      g:
      b.   0.00134
      d.   6.84
      e.   85.4
      g.   10.84
      h.   9.05
      i.   0.00165
      cg:
      a.   10,000
      b.   0.134
      c.   1.011
      d.   684
      f.   3.79
      g.   1,084
      i.   0.165
      mg:
      a.   100,000
      c.   10.11
      d.   6,840
      e.   85,400
      f.   37.9
      h.   9,050
      i.   1.65

II. SECTION TWO

2.1 Answers will vary.

2.2 width:
21.6 cm. = 216 mm.
length:
27.9 cm. = 279 mm.

2.3 a. length
b. mass
c. mass
d. mass
e. volume
f. volume
g. volume
h. volume
i. volume
j. volume
k. temperature
l. length

2.4 a. 21.60 cm.
b. 0.02cm
c. 27.90 cm.
d. 0.02cm

2.5 Answers may vary.

2.6 Measurements will vary.

Answers will vary. Examples:
2.7 a. 50 ml burette ± 0.01 ml
b. gas measuring tube ± 0.1 ml
c. 10 ml pipette ± 0.01 ml
d. 10 ml cylinder ± 0.01 ml
e. 50 ml cylinder ± 0.1 ml
f. 100 ml cylinder ± 0.1 ml

2.8 Answers will vary.

2.9 adult check

2.10 Summaries will vary.

2.11 Choices will vary.

III. SECTION THREE

3.1 Hint:
The observations of each person must
be evaluated separately. Different
people will draw different conclusions.

3.2 Hint:
Include the wind factor as part of
your answer.

3.3 Observations will vary.

3.4 Answers will vary, but must match
with 3.3.

3.5 a. There is no specific answer.
Observations will vary.
b. Answers will vary but must be
consistent with facts observed.
c. Hint:
Hypothesis must be logical and
reasonable.

3.6 The flask with the candle gases
should change the limewater to a
cloudy white mixture. The control
should remain colorless and un-
changed.

3.7 The control is the standard of
comparison and is used to check to
see what a change in the experiment
does to the experiment.

3.8 A cloudy film forms on top. When
swirled, the liquid becomes cloudy
as did the candle gases but with
less intensity.

3.9 The results are the same as the candle,
but less in amount

3.10 yes; the reactions were the same.

3.11 The candle container;
Example:
Candle produced something that is
in the air.

3.12 candle; the reaction was greater
and faster.

3.13 Some results occur.

3.14 water and carbon dioxide; carbon
dioxide; of course; carbon dioxide

3.15 The candle is burning and produces
carbon dioxide as a product.

3.16   k = 65.6

3.17   a. 0.5; 4
       b. 1; 8
       c. 2; 16
       d. 3; 24

3.18   a. 18
       b. 9
       c. 6
       d. 3
       e. 2
       f. 1

3.19

3.20   81.4

IV.   SECTION FOUR

4.1   a. 3
       b. 3
       c. 3
       d. 5
       e. 3
       f. 4
       g. 4
       h. 2
       i. 4
       j. 6

4.2   23.46
4.3   0.064

4.4   0.095

4.5   6.36

4.6   a. 3.24×10^{4}
       b. 5.43×10^{-4}
       c. 1.3×10^{-13}
       d. 1.8×10^{1}

4.7   a. .00897
       b. 3
       c. 34,000
       d. 602,000,000,000,000,000,000,000

4.8   a. 9.6×10^{14}
       b. 1.2×10^{28}
       c. 2×10^{8}
       d. 2.0×10^{9}
       e. 6.9×10^{10}
       f. 2.0×10^{27}
       g. 4.7×10^{-18} or 5×10^{-18}

V.   SECTION FIVE

5.1   Articles will vary.

5.2   research, develop new chemicals, quality control

5.3   synthetic fibers, paints, drugs, cosmetics, lubricants

5.4   offices and laboratories

5.5   manufacturing and research firms

5.6   extensive education, Phd. level work is expected

5.7   average

5.8   They work in manufacturing.

5.9   design equipment and process to
       mass-produce chemicals

5.10   offices, laboratories, and
       manufacturing plants

5.11   chemical production facilities and
       government

5.12   extensive education in science and
       mathematics

5.13   average

5.14   Many of the tests, models, and data are
       run through computers.

5.15   This is a growth industry with many
       available jobs for people who are willing
       to relocate.

1.1 **adult check**

1.2 Either order:
a. pure substances
b. mixture

1.3 Either order:
a. elements
b. compounds

1.4 Any order:
a. discover universal cure for disease
b. discover ways to prolong life
c. transmute base elements (lead) to gold

1.5 Alexandria, Egypt

1.6 They are begun with capital letters.

1.7 A second letter is added which is different.

1.8 Latin

1.9 Cu - Copper
Pb - Lead
Hg - Mercury
Ag - Silver
Au - Gold

1.10 yes   Al
yes   Zn
no   C
yes   Fe
yes   Cu
no   S

1.11 metal
metal
non-metal (conducts a little)
metal
metal
non-metal

1.12 Ag_2O $CaBr_2$

KCl   CsI

AlF_3 $SiBr_4$

SnO_2

1.13 **adult check**

1.14 a.   <u>METALS</u>
light metals   =12
transition metals =44
aluminum   = 1
lanthanide series =15
actinide series   =15
Total   87

b.   <u>NONMETALS</u>
nonmetals   =15
noble gases   = 6
hydrogen   = 1
Total =22

1.15 Metals are in lower left with nonmetals in upper right.

II. SECTION TWO

2.1 Answers will vary.

2.2 a. Dye slowly spreads across the bottom and throughout the container.
b. The tablet has completely dissolved, and the color is evenly distributed throughout the container.
c. Water molecules have dispersed dye molecules throughout beaker.

2.3 The color spreads rapidly in the hot container and <u>very</u> slowly in the ice water.

2.4 a. hot
b. hot
c. increase
d. The hotter the particles, the faster they move.

2.5 A substance with only one kind of particle.

2.6 Example:
Because the hot water particles are moving faster, they mix the colored particles faster throughout the container.

typical data:

2.7 0:00 - 25.0; 76.2   Observations:
0:30 - 40.2; 75.8
1:00 - 48.4; 74.6
1:30 - 50.2; 73.4   Solid begins
2.00 - 51.0; 72.0   to melt
2:30 - 52.2; 71.2
3:00 - 52.4; 70.4
3:30 - 52.6; 69.4   Solid about ½
4:00 - 52.8; 68.2   melted

4:30 - 53.0; 67.2
5:00 - 53.0; 66.4
5:30 - 53.0; 65.4
6:00 - 53.8; 64.6
6:30 - 54.8; 63.6   Solid totally
7:00 - 56.0; 62.8   melted
7:30 - 60.2; 60.8

2.8   Since both are the same tempera-
       ture, the heat exchange will now
       occur at the same rate with the
       air environment.

       Typical data:

0:00 - 76.0; 26.0   Observations
0:30 - 70.0; 26.4
1:00 - 61.0; 26.8
1:30 - 56.2; 27.6   Solid begins
2:00 - 55.4; 28.4   to form.
2:30 - 54.0; 29.0
3:00 - 53.2; 29.8
3:30 - 53.2; 30.4
4:00 - 53.0; 31.0
4:30 - 53.0; 31.8
5:00 - 53.0; 32.4
5:30 - 52.8; 33.0   Solid-liquid =
6:00 - 52.8; 33.6   ½ and ½
7:00 - 52.6; 34.8
7:30 - 52.4; 35.4
8:00 - 52.4; 36.0   Nearly all
8:30 - 51.4; 36.4   solid.
9:00 - 50.0; 36.8
9:30 - 48.2; 37.2   All solid
10:00 - 46.0; 37.8
10:30 - 44.0; 38.2
11:00 - 41.0; 38.6
11:30 - 39.6; 39.0
12:00 - 39.6; 39.2

2.9   a. adult check

       b. adult check

       c. adult check

       d. The melting curve for
          paradichlorobenzene.

2.10   a. solid
       b. melting
       c. liquid
       d. 53.0

2.11   Temperature of PDCB is going up,
       and the water temperature is going
       down.

2.12   a. hot water (burner)
       b. The water temperature is going
          down.

2.13   a. 1
       b. 3
       c. the temperature is rising

2.14   The environment is hotter than
       the PDCB - therefore transferring
       energy to the PDCB. Also the
       temperature continues to decrease.

2.15   a. 2
       b. added energy with no tempera-
          ture increase

2.16   flat or horizontal

2.17   a. temperature (^{o}C) and time
          (minutes)
       b. Changes in the physical
          nature of PDCB or similar title
       c. teacher check
       d. 53.0
       e. yes
       f. yes
       g. because they are opposite
          processes - mirror images
          of the same energy transfer
          process

2.18   a. decrease
       b. kinetic
       c. There is a temperature change.

2.19   This is a potential energy change
       as the liquid changes to a solid.
       The "stored" energy in the liquid
       is lost so the particles can
       become a solid.

2.20   The particles are slowing down as
       a solid so kinetic energy is
       being lost, as evidenced by the
       decrease in temperature.

2.21   a. neither
       b. The energy transfer necessary
          to melt or solidify is not
          taking place; so, at a constant
          energy state the substance can-
          not melt or turn more solid.

2.22 a. more
      b. more

2.23 a. yes
      b. no
      c. A physical change only changes shape, size, or structure, not the phase of the substance.

2.24 a. yes
      b. yes
      c. yes
      d. Cool them off (change or reverse the energy flow).

2.25 a. The solder melts and when cool turns back to a solid.
      b. When the original temperature is regained, the solder is returned to its original state.

2.26 Hint:
      Suggest dissolving the sulfur, leaving the iron behind; evaporating the sulfur dioxide to leave the sulfur behind; use a magnet to attract the iron and leave the sulfur behind.

2.27 a. various shapes and sizes, various shades and colors
      b. crystalline cubes--white to colorless, all cubes alike

2.28 sand

2.29 **adult check**
      a. Hint:
         Base your plan on dissolving properties of salt and non-dissolving properties of sand.
      b. Answers will vary.
      c. about ½ gram
      d. about ½ gram

2.30 phase

2.31 chemical

2.32 chemical, physical

2.33 phase

2.34 physical

2.35 chemical

2.36 chemical, physical

2.37 physical

2.38 chemical, physical

2.39 chemical, physical, phase

2.40 0

2.41 I

2.42 I

2.43 0

2.44 0

2.45 I

2.46 0

2.47 0

2.48 I

2.49 0

2.50 I

2.51 I

2.52 0

2.53 0

2.54 I

III. SECTION THREE

3.1 Diagram

3.2 The oil layers out on the top. Some droplets form from the oil but soon break up to form a layer on top of the water.

3.3 a. heterogeneous
     b. not as done
     c. It is not possible with this mixing method to get small enough or disperse enough oil droplets to keep the oil suspended in the water or vinegar.

3.4   The liquid does not let the oil
      separate into a separate layer as
      before.

3.5   more homogeneous

3.6   The droplets are smaller and the
      egg, salt, sugar, and mustard help
      to keep the oil from rejoining
      to form the single oil layer.

3.7   a. no
      b. The components form a
         heterogeneous mixture while
         a solution is a homogeneous
         mixture.

3.8   **adult check**

3.9   a. fat
      b. water (milk)

3.10 a. The milk coagulates and gets
         "stiff."
      b. Addition of acid increased the
         size of the particles so they
         could form a solid and come
         together.
      c. They are the same.

3.11 a. no
      b. because the fresh milk has the
         fat particles which will separ-
         ate out and float to the top
         of the container.

3.12 Heterogeneous mixtures have large
      particles that separate out;
      homogeneous mixtures have small
      suspended particles; and solutions
      have very small particles that
      will not separate out.

3.13 a. Suspensions are mixtures with
         large particles suspended in
         a medium. These suspended
         particles will separate out
         under the influence of gravity
         if left alone. This suspen-
         sion interrupts a beam of
         light completely.

      b. A colloid is an evenly dis-
         tributed mixture that has
         suspended particles too small
         to separate out by natural
         gravitational forces. The
         average size is 10^{-6} to 10^{-8}

cm particle diameter. This particle size disperses and refracts
light but does not totally block
the light beam.

3.14 Jar 1
      2.2, color begins to move down,
      colorless
      Jar 2
      4.6, several colors begin to ap-
      pear, colorless
      Jar 3
      7.0, red moving faster than blue,
      colorless
      Jar 4
      9.2,
      reddish
      Jar 5
      11.4,
      reddish
      Jar 6
      13.8,
      about a 5 cm spread in color,
      reddish
      Jar 7
      16.0,
      purple
      Jar 8
      18.4,
      purple
      Jar 9
      20.8,
      purple
      Jar 10
      23.2,
      blue
      Jar 11
      25.6, no reddish color remains,
      blue
      Jar 12
      28.0,
      blue
      Jar 13
      30.0,
      blue
      Jar 14
      0, sand clear white again,
      colorless
      Jar 15
      0,
      colorless

Typical data:

3.15 a. Jar 1   1
         Jar 2   1
         Jar 3   1
         Jar 4   2
         Jar 5   4
         Jar 6   6
         Jar 7   8
         Jar 8   9
         Jar 9 10
         Jar 10   8
         Jar 11   6
         Jar 12   4
         Jar 13   2
         Jar 14   1
         Jar 15   1

      b. adult check

3.16 a. no

      b. no

      c. The grape drink was made up of
          several different substances, each
          separating out at a different rate.

3.17 adult check
      (Should include the idea that
      substances added to the soil may
      take years to move downward and
      enter the underground water supply.)

3.18 nitrogen

3.19 adult check

1.1 Liquids assume the shape of their container and only fill as high as the top surface of the liquid. However, gases expand to fill whatever volume is available.

1.2 diffusion

1.3 moving

1.4 a. liquids
    b. liquids
    c. gases

1.5 a. elastic
    b. energy

1.6 a. vibrate
    b. rotate
    c. line

1.7 pressure

1.8 adult check

1.9 For molecules of the same mass, their kinetic energy is proportional to their velocity (K.E. α V). Therefore, the average K.E. occurs on the graph at their average velocity.

1.10 horizontal axis (speed)

1.11 The temperature of the sample is proportional to its average kinetic energy, which for particles of equal mass is measured by their speed.

1.12 adult check

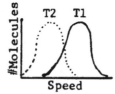

1.13 T_1 has a higher average K.E. than T_2. The points x and y reflect the temperatures of the two systems respectively. There will be many slower molecules and few faster ones.

Examples 1.14–1.16

1.14 a. increase heat (temperature)
     b. increase surface area or remove vapor

1.15 a. remove heat (lower temperature)
     b. reduce surface area or cover

1.16 an increase in surface area or removal of vapor

1.17 The water level will go down.

1.18 The water level will go down due to evaporation (loss of water).

1.19 The molecules will cool and slow down.

1.20 no

1.21 Hint:
     should include evaporation countered by condensation

1.22 increase

1.23 It is called a pressure cooker because the evaporated water caused added pressure in the container which elevates the boiling temperature.

1.24 A

1.25 Because in B the evaporated water cannot escape as it can in A.

1.26 Because the return process (condensation) cannot occur in an open system.

1.27 Even frozen foods have a few molecules that have enough energy to evaporate. When they do, the chances of them collecting on the freezer sides as frost are greater than returning to the food. Therefore, the food dries out.

1.28 Evaporation removes the fast, high energy molecules. When these are removed, the resulting liquid is less hot and therefore feels cooler.

1.29 The ice causes the water vapor inside the container to condense, thus lowering the total pressure on the inside of the container. The reduced pressure allows the liquid to exceed the pressure necessary to boil.

1.30 The vacuum pump removes air molecules and reduces the pressure on the liquid. The reduced pressure allows the liquid to reach the vapor pressure necessary to boil at a much lower temperature.

1.31 Yes, it is possible to have the blood boil because the rapid decrease in pressure may allow the blood to reach its boiling point at the reduced pressure.

II. SECTION TWO

2.1 Example data:
a. 100 g
b. 0   12.1
c. 100/g; 10.8
d. 300/g; 9.8
e. 500/g; 9.1
f. 700/g; 8.5
g. 900/g; 8.0
h. 1100/g; 7.5
i. 1300/g; 7.1
j. 1500/g; 6.8
k. 1700/g; 6.5
l. 1900/g; 6.2
m. 2100/g; 6.0
n. 2300/g; 5.8
o. 2500/g; 5.6
p. 2700/g; 5.5
q. 2900/g; 5.4
r. 3100/g; 5.3
s. 0   12.1

2.2 **adult check**

2.3 As the pressure increases, the volume decreases.

2.4 No heat was added and the heat generated from the compression was easily dissipated over the investigation.

2.5 yes

2.6 The two zero values are 12.1 which indicates a constant number of molecules (**no gas gained or lost**).

2.7 a. variable
b. constant
c. variable
d. constant

2.8 The friction of the syringe could be decreased by a lubricant. Any loss of gas could be minimized by a better seal. The mass errors could be corrected by accurately measuring the masses prior to placing them on the hanger.

2.9 a. yes
b. Since the molecules now need to travel less distance to hit the wall, they will collide with the wall more frequently, thus causing more pressure.

2.10 a. The gas pressure increases.
b. By definition, pressure is the number of collisions per unit time.

2.11 a. larger
b. smaller
c. 6.0 ml
d. (9.0 ml)(500 mm Hg) = (x)(750 mm Hg)
$$x = \frac{(9\ ml)(500)}{750} = \underline{6\ ml}$$

2.12 a. smaller
b. larger
c. (180 cc)(300 mm Hg) = (90 cc)(x)
$$x = \frac{(180)(300\ mm\ Hg)}{90\ cc} = \underline{600\ mm\ Hg}$$

2.13 a. decrease
b. increase
c. (4 liters)(700 mm Hg) = (x)(100 mm Hg)
$$x = \frac{(4\ liters)(700)}{100} = \underline{28}\ L$$

2.14 **adult check**

2.15 Example:
a. The substances will respond because the outside pressure is reduced which allows the bubbles to expand.
b. varies
c. The marshmallow decreased because when the marshmallow expanded, it stretched and some of the trapped gas escaped. When the atmospheric pressure was reapplied, less air was inside to cause pressure to hold up the marshmallow in its original form.
d. Basically, the same thing applies here as with the marshmallow.

2.16 (12.5 L)(42.0 cm Hg) = (x)(75.0 cm Hg)
$$x = \frac{(12.5\ L)(42.0)}{75.0} = \underline{7.00\ L}$$

2.17 $(450 \text{ cm}^3)(1 \text{ atm}) = (48 \text{ cm}^3)(x)$
$x = \dfrac{(450)(1 \text{ atm})}{48} = \underline{9 \text{ atm}}$

2.18 $(190 \text{ ml})(740 \text{ mm Hg}) = (760 \text{ mm Hg})(x)$
$x = \dfrac{(190 \text{ ml})(740)}{(760)} = \underline{185 \text{ ml}}$

III. SECTION THREE

3.1   a. hot car, 33°C, 68.7cm
       b. room, 24°C, 67.0cm
       c. refrigerator, 8°C, 65.2cm
       d. freezer, -5°C, 62.8cm

3.2   increase

3.3   direct

3.4   yes

3.5   The circumference would continue to decrease until it reached zero.

3.6   Did not measure accurately, not ideal conditions, balloon elasticity varies with temperature, measurements changed during data collection, some gas may have leaked out during the investigation.

3.7   a. 291
       b. 336
       c. 556

3.8   a. 369
       b. 398
       c. 709

3.9   a. decreased
       b. smaller
       c. 540 liters
       d. $\dfrac{600 \text{ L}}{300°K} = \dfrac{x}{270°K}$
$(270°K)(600L) = (300°K)(K)$
$x = \dfrac{(270)(600)}{300} = 540 \text{ L}$

3.10   a. increased
       b. increased
       c. 300°K
       d. $\dfrac{200ml}{200°K} = \dfrac{300ml}{x}$
$(200ml)(K) = (200°K)(300ml)$
$x = \dfrac{(200°K)(300)}{200}$
$= \underline{300°K}$

3.11 $\dfrac{2.5 \text{ l}}{250°K} = \dfrac{x}{450°K}$
$(250°K)(x) = (2.5L)(450°K)$
$x = \dfrac{(2.5L)(450)}{250} = 4.5L$

3.12 When the gas increases in temperature, the average kinetic energy increases. This means the average speed has increased. Since the speed has increased, the molecules hit the wall harder and more frequently. This causes added force in the walls, and since the pressure on the outside remains constant, the container expands in size.

3.13   0

3.14   no

3.15   Since temperature is a measure of average kinetic energy of a system and there is no kinetic energy at 0°K, there can be no temperature below 0°K.

3.16   This report will depend upon the reference used.

IV. SECTION FOUR

4.1 $\dfrac{P_1 V_1}{P_2} = V_i ; \quad \dfrac{T_1 V_2}{T_2} = V_i$

$\dfrac{P_1 V_1}{P_2} = \dfrac{T_1 V_2}{T_2}$

$\dfrac{P_1 V_1}{T_1 P_2} = \dfrac{V_2}{T_2}$

$\dfrac{P_1 V_1}{T_1} = \dfrac{P_2 V_2}{T_2}$

4.2   a. 740 mm Hg
       b. 10.0 liters
       c. 300
       d. 370 mm Hg
       e. 200
$\dfrac{(740 \text{ mm Hg})(10.0 \text{ liters})}{300°K} =$
$\dfrac{(370 \text{ mm Hg})(V_2)}{200°K}$
$V_2 = \dfrac{(740)(10.0 \text{ liters})(200)}{(300)(370)} = \underline{13.3L}$

4.3 $$\frac{(16 \text{ volume})(1 \text{ atm})}{305^{0}\text{K}} = \frac{(1 \text{ volume})(48 \text{ atm})}{x}$$

$(16)(1)(T_2) \quad (305^{0}\text{K})(1)(48)$

$$(T_2) = \frac{(305^{0}\text{K})(1)(48)}{(16)(1)} = \underline{915^{0}\text{K}}$$

4.4 $$\frac{(25L)(1 \text{ atm})}{373^{0}\text{K}} = \frac{(V_2)(20 \text{ mm Hg})}{298^{0}\text{K}}$$

$$V_2 = \frac{(25L)(760)(298)}{(373)(20)}$$

$V_2 = \underline{760 \text{ L}}$ $1 \text{ atm} = 760 \text{ mm Hg}$

4.5 $$\frac{(0.5m^3)(760 \text{ mm Hg})}{(306^{0}\text{K})} = \frac{(0.1m^3)(P_2)}{223^{0}\text{K}}$$

$$P_2 = \frac{(0.5)(760 \text{ mm Hg})(223)}{(306)(0.1)}$$

$P_2 = \underline{2769 \text{ mm Hg}}$

4.6 $$\frac{(20L)(5,000 \text{ mm Hg})}{303^{0}\text{K}} = \frac{(V_2)(760 \text{ mm Hg})}{273^{0}\text{K}}$$

$$V_2 \quad \frac{(20L)(5000)(273)}{(303)(760)}$$

$V_2 = \underline{119L}$

4.7 $$\frac{(300 \text{ cc})(760 \text{ mm Hg})}{(273^{\circ}\text{K})} = \frac{(V_2)(1520 \text{mm Hg})}{(2473^{\circ}\text{K})}$$

$$V_2 = \frac{(300)(760)(2473)\text{cc}}{(273)(1520)}$$

$V_2 = \underline{1358\text{cc}}$

4.8 $$\frac{(0.360L)(2.3 \text{ atm})}{298^{0}\text{K}} = \frac{(V_2)(1 \text{ atm})}{273^{0}\text{K}}$$

$$V_2 = \frac{(0.360)(2.3)(273)}{298} = 0.76L$$

4.9 $$\frac{(2.5L)(7.80)}{330} = \frac{(V_2)(750)}{290}$$

$$V_2 = \frac{(2.5)(7.80)(290)}{(330)(750)} = \underline{0.023L}$$

4.10 **adult check**

V. SECTION FIVE

5.1 a. slower
b. lower

5.2 yes

5.3 **Both times the rubber band was pulled back the same distance; therefore, it provides the same energy to each ball**

5.4 Either order:
a. mass
b. velocity

5.5 **yes**

5.6 Because both have the same energy (heat content) so both have the same energy of motion. Also, since

temperature is a measure of kinetic energy and both are at the same temperature, both have the same kinetic energy.

5.7 yes

5.8 no

5.9 Since the masses are different their velocities will be different, in the ratio of K.E. $= \frac{1}{2} mv^2$.

5.10 yes

5.11 different gases

5.12 a. 0.10 g
b. 250 ml
c. 0.50 g
d. 250 ml
e. 0.50 g
f. 500 ml

5.13 A and B

5.14 Avogadro's hypothesis

5.15 32.0 g; 2.0 g; 17.2 g; 28.0 g; 44.0 g

5.16 yes

5.17 Each is the same volume under the same conditions -- Avogadro's Hypothesis.

5.18 10/5 = 2/1

5.19 2/1

5.20 15 g

5.21 3

5.22 3

5.23 10

5.24 a. 20
b. 10

5.25 15 g; 5 g; 25 g; 2 g

5.26 a. 67.2
b. 44.8

5.27 1 mole

5.28   6 g

5.29   1 mole

5.30   28 g

5.31   34 g

5.32   2 moles

5.33   17 g

5.34 A_3B

5.35   **Since three volumes of A–A react with one volume of B–B to yield two volumes of product, and since equal volumes have equal numbers of molecules (Avogadro's Hypothesis), the molecular formula of the product is A_3B. Or 6 A's and 2 B's must be divided equally into 2 parts; thus, A_3B.**

5.36   a. hydrogen
       b. nitrogen
       c. ammonia

5.37 $3H_2 + N_2 \rightarrow 2NH_3$

5.38 $3A + 1B \rightarrow 2A_3B.$
       2   2

5.39   H + H H + O → H H +
       H   O   O   H O
                              H

       $\underline{2}\ H$ $+\ \underline{1}\ O$ $\rightarrow \underline{2}\ H\ O$
         2(g)   2(g)   2 (g)

5.40   1; 2

5.41   2; 1; 2

5.42   2; 1; 2

5.43   2; 1; 2

5.44   22.4; 44.8

5.45 $1\ Cl_2 + 1\ H_2 \rightarrow 2\ HCl$

5.46 $2\ NO_2 \rightarrow N_2O_4$

5.47 $1\ C_3H_8 + 5\ O_2 \rightarrow 3\ CO_2 + 4\ H_2O$

5.48   a. 2; 1; 2
       b. 2; 1; 1; 1
       c. 2; 1; 1; 2
       d. 1; 6; 4

5.49   a. ½; 1
       b. 5; 10
       c. 1
       d. 22.4

5.50   **adult check**

5.51   **adult check**

5.52   **adult check**

5.53   a. H
       b. 1.00797
       c. 1.00797
       d. 0
       e. 15.9994
       f. 15.9994
       g. Ca
       h. 40.08
       i. 40.08
       j. U
       k. 238.03
       l. 238.03
       m. Cl
       n. 35.453
       o. 35.453
       p. Fe
       q. 55.847
       r. 55.847
       s. P
       t. 30.9738
       u. 30.9738
       v. S
       w. 32.064
       x. 32.064
       y. N
       z. 14.0067
     aa. 14.0067

5.54   10

5.55   1:1

5.56   20

5.57   2:1

5.58   1,000

5.59   1:1

5.60 $N\ (6.02 \times 10^{23})$

5.61   1:1

5.62   2:1

5.52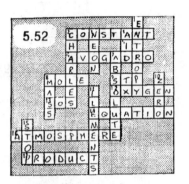

5.63   1:2

5.64   10

5.65   1

5.66   2

5.67   2

5.68   a. 1,000
       b. 2,000
       c. 2,000

5.69   a. 1 mole
       b. 2 moles
       c. 2 moles

5.70   a. 1:2:2
       b. BN_2W_2
       c. B= 100
          2N= 370
          2W= 48
          518 g/mole

5.71 B_2NW_4

5.72   2 B = 200
       1 N = 175
       4 W = 96
              471 g/mole

5.73   a. CO = 28 g
       b. U_2O_5 = 556 g

5.74   26.98 g

5.75   31.773 g

5.76   5.7474 g

5.77   2.0183 g

5.78   68.67 g

5.79   476.06 g

5.80   512.1142 g

5.81   366.7512 g

5.82   32 g

5.83   28 g

5.84   2 g

5.85   18 x 2 = 36 g

5.86   4 g

5.87   32 g

5.88   no

5.89   carbon atoms

5.90   hydrogen atoms

5.91   oxygen atoms

5.92   The respective numbers of atoms of C, H, and O in the molecule.

5.93   a. H; 1; Cl; 1; --; --; 36.5
       b. Na; 2; C; 1; O; 3; 106.0
       c. Ba; 1; N; 2; O; 6; 261.3
       d. C; 6; H; 12; O; 6; 180.0
       e. Fe; 2; O; 3; --; --; 159.6
       f. H; 2; S; 1; O; 4; 98.0
       g. Ag; 1; N; 1; O; 3; 169.9
       h. H; 2; O; 1; --; --; 18.0

5.94   let x = length of 1 side
       volume = x^3 = 22.4 liters x $\frac{1000cc}{liter}$
       $\frac{22.4 \times 10^3 cc}{}$
       x = $\sqrt[3]{22.4 \times 10^3 cc}$ = $\sqrt[3]{22.4 \times 10 cm}$
       2.82 x 10 cm =   28.2 cm/side
       adult check

5.95   a. 2; 2; 1
       b. 1; 4; 2; 2
       c. 2; 2; 2; 1
       d. 4; 1; 3; 2

5.96   a. 30.0
       b. 46.0
       c. 58.5
       d. 136.1
       e. 352.0
       f. 148.3
       g. 63.0
       h. 330.0
       i. 17.0
       j. 231.4
       k. 62.0
       l. 44.0

5.97   **adult check**
       $Cu + \underline{4}HNO_3 + Cu(NO_3)_2 + \underline{2}NO_2 + \underline{2}H$

5.98   **Cu:Cu(NO3) = 1:1**
       Mole wt Cu = 63.5
       g.f.w. Cu(NO3)2 = 187.5

       $\frac{63.5g\ Cu}{187.5g\ Cu(NO_3)_2} = \frac{1.5g\ Cu}{(x)Cu(NO_3)_2}$

       $x = \frac{(1.5)(187.5)}{63.5}$

       = 4.4g Cu(NO3)2 needed

5.99 acid

5.100 HNO_3

5.101 10

5.102 basic

5.103 **adult check**

5.104 2; 2

5.105 1; 1; 1

5.106 **adult check**

5.107 1; 1; 1; 1

5.108 The Zn reacts with the Cu in solution to form Cu atoms. The Cu in solution is blue, and when all the color is gone, all the Cu in solution has turned to Cu atoms.

5.109 Hint:
Test a pinch of Zn in a test tube with a little 3M $H_2 SO_4$
This reaction fizzes.

5.110 1; 1; 1; 1

5.111 **Example:**
1.5 ± 0.1 g = 0.024 moles
2.3 ± 0.1 g
0.9 ± 0.1 g
1.4 ± 0.2 g = **0.023 moles**

5.112 $\dfrac{1.4}{1.5}$ x 100 = 93.5%

5.113 **adult check**

5.114 **adult check**

5.115 **adult check**

5.116 a. 2; 2; 1
b. 2; 2; 1
c. 2; 2; 4; 1
d. 1; 2; 1; 1
e. 2; 2; 2; 1
f. 1; 2; 1; 1
g. 4; 3; 2
h. 1; 1; 1
i. 1; 1; 1

5.117 12.01 g = 1 mole = mass of 6.02×10^{23} atoms
$\dfrac{12.01\ g}{6.02 \times 10^{23}\ atom}$ = 2×10^{-23} g/atom

5.118 6.02×10^{20} Mg atoms = 0.001 mole
1 mole Mg = 24.31g
Therefore 0.001 mole = 0.0243g =
2.43×10^{-2} g

5.119 $Al_2 S_3$
2.70g = 0.1 mole Al
$\dfrac{Al}{S} = \dfrac{2}{3} = \dfrac{0.1}{x}$
x = 0.15 mole = 4.80g S

5.120 Assume 100g sample, then 2.68g = Mg.
$\dfrac{2.68g}{24.31g/mole}$ = 0.110 moles
$\dfrac{6.02 \times 10^{23}}{1\ mole} = \dfrac{x}{0.110\ moles}$
x = 6.62×10^{22} atoms

5.121 Assume 100g sample.
67.3% = 67.3g C to 4.6% = 4.6 g N
$\dfrac{67.3gC}{12.01g/mole}$ = 5.60 mole C
$\dfrac{4.6\ g\ N}{14.01g/mole}$ = 0.33 moles
$\dfrac{C}{N} = \dfrac{5.60}{0.33} = \dfrac{x}{1}$
x = 17.0

5.122 Daily dose = (12 tablets)(0.3240 g/tablet) = 3.888g/day
g.f.w. of aspirin = $C_9H_8O_4$
(12 x 9)+(1 x 8)+(16 x 4) = 180
$\dfrac{3.888g}{180\ g/m} = \dfrac{x}{6.02 \times 10^{23}\ \frac{molecules}{mole}}$
x = $\dfrac{(3.888)(6.02 \times 10^{23})}{180}$ =
1.30032×10^{22}

5.123 $\dfrac{Ce}{O} = \dfrac{2}{3}$
$\dfrac{2.00g\ Ce}{140.12\ g/mole}$ = 0.0142 mole
$\dfrac{Ce}{O} = \dfrac{2}{3} = \dfrac{0.0142}{x}$

x = 0.0214 mole O = 0.0107 moles O_2
(0.0107 moles O_2) $\dfrac{32g}{mole}$ = **0.343 gO_2**

$\dfrac{0.0107\ mole}{y} = \dfrac{1\ mole}{22.4L}$

y = **.239L**

5.124 Assume 100g sample.

$\dfrac{74.0g}{12.0} = 6.2$ moles C

$\dfrac{8.7g}{1.0} = 8.7$ moles H

$\dfrac{17.3}{14.0} = 1.2$ moles N

$C_{6.2} H_{8.7} N_{1.2} = C_5 H_7 N_1$

C:H:N = 5:7:1

5.125 34g $Al_2O_3 = 1/3$ mole

$\dfrac{O_2}{Al_2O_3} = \dfrac{3}{2} = \dfrac{x}{1/3}$

$x = \frac{1}{2}$ mole = <u>11.2L</u>

5.126 61g $KClO_3 = \frac{1}{2}$ mole

$\dfrac{KClO_3}{O_2} = \dfrac{2}{3} = \dfrac{\frac{1}{2}}{x}$

$2x = 1.5$

$x = 0.75$ moles

1.1 Democritus

1.2 third or fourth B.C.

1.3 studied under Leucippus of Abdera; studied in Egypt, Chaldea, Babylon, Persia, specialized in astronomy

1.4 Matter was made of indivisible indestructable particles. They differed from each other in shape.

1.5 Socrates

1.6 John Dalton

1.7 Two atoms can combine in different ratios; e.g., 1:1, 1:2, 2:1, and so on, to produce different substances.

1.8 Atoms can combine only in combinations of whole atoms. Therefore, matter can combine only in fixed mass ratios.

1.9 Atoms are alike in everything except their mass; atoms are indestructable.

1.10 no

1.11 no

1.12 Since the final products are different from each other and some are different from their starting characteristics, it is apparent that each reacts differently to oxygen.

1.13 nothing happens

1.14 Again, no reaction is apparent.

1.15 nothing happens

1.16 These two strips now repel each other.

1.17 They actively attract each other. The A-1 attracts the V-2 as the A-1 rotates to meet or touch V-2.

1.18 Again, they attract each other. The V-1 rotates to meet A-2.

1.19 a. repel
b. attract
c. attract
d. repel

1.20 a. yes
b. yes
c. no
d. repel
e. attract

1.21 **adult check**

1.22 **adult check**

1.23 a volume of positive charge with negative electrons

1.24 cathode ray tube

1.25 Ne-22 and Ne-20 have different masses.

1.26 Thomson discovered a finite unit charge. All charges are multiples of the unit charge.

1.27 pitchblende

1.28 a. Roentgen
b. Becquerel

1.29 a. radium
b. polonium

1.30 the Sorbonne

1.31 a. discovery of radium and polonium (1903)
b. isolation of radium (1911)

1.32 J.J. Thomson

1.33 a. alpha particles
b. helium nuclei

1.34 a. beta particles
b. electrons from nucleus

1.35 a. gamma rays
b. electromagnetic (high energy) radiation (waves)

1.36 Starting with uranium, each radioactive element decays until a stable daughter element is reached.

1.37 Rutherford fired alpha particles at gold foil. Most passed through; some were deflected and some bounced back.

1.38 geiger counter

1.39 Ernest Rutherford

1.40 The electron - a negatively - charged particle in the atom.

1.41 The nucleus around which electrons orbited.

1.42 The quantum atom - electrons have fixed orbits.

1.43 Electrons appear to orbit the nucleus as planets orbit the sun.

1.44 Electrons fall from high energy states to low energy states. Energy difference is emitted.

1.45 The frequencies of light in line spectra represent changes in energy levels.

1.46 Schrodinger explained electron orbits in terms of wave function developing a mathematical model.

1.47 All matter has particle characteristics and wave characteristics.

1.48 a. very small - like atoms
b. very fast - approaching the speed of light

1.49 waves

1.50 helium nucleus - two protons plus two neutrons

1.51 alpha bombardment dislodged neutrons

1.52 not much

1.53 First bowling ball would be moved.

1.54 Mass of neutron must be nearly the mass of a proton.

1.55 a. -1
b. Thomson
c. 1895
d. 1/1837
e. outside nucleus

1.56 a. +1
b. Rutherford
c. 1906
d. 1
e. nucleus

1.57 a. 0
b. Chadwick
c. 1932
d. 1
e. nucleus

1.58   a.   7
      b.   because each has the same number of protons

1.59   a.   14, 15
      b.   because the number of neutrons is different, one with 7 and the other with 8

1.60   a.   7, 7
      b.   because the protons and electrons are equal in neutral atoms

1.61   a.   2
      b.   2

1.62   a.   2
      b.   2

1.63   a.   6
      b.   3
      c.   3
      d.   3
      e.   3

1.64   a.   3
      b.   7
      c.   3
      d.   4
      e.   3
      f.   3

1.65   a.   4
      b.   9
      c.   4
      d.   5
      e.   4
      f.   4

1.66   a.   5
      b.   10
      c.   5
      d.   5
      e.   5
      f.   5

1.67   a.   5
      b.   11
      c.   5
      d.   6
      e.   5
      f.   5

1.68   a.   6
      b.   12
      c.   6
      d.   6
      e.   6
      f.   6

1.69   a.   6
      b.   13
      c.   6
      d.   7
      e.   6
      f.   6

1.70   a.   7
      b.   14
      c.   7
      d.   7
      e.   7
      f.   7

1.71   a.   7
      b.   15
      c.   7
      d.   8
      e.   7
      f.   7

1.72   a.   8
      b.   16
      c.   8
      d.   8
      e.   8
      f.   8

1.73   a.   8
      b.   17
      c.   8
      d.   9
      e.   8
      f.   8

1.74   a.   8
      b.   18
      c.   8
      d.   10
      e.   8
      f.   8

1.75   a.   9
      b.   19
      c.   9
      d.   10
      e.   9
      f.   9

1.76 a. 17
      b. 35
      c. 17
      d. 18
      e. 17
      f. 17

1.77 a. 17
      b. 37
      c. 17
      d. 20
      e. 17
      f. 17

1.78 a. 92
      b. 235
      c. 92
      d. 143
      e. 92
      f. 92

1.79 a. 92
      b. 238
      c. 92
      d. 146
      e. 92
      f. 92

1.80 Across:
      1. electron
      6. same
      7. on
      8. P
      9. Cr
      10. money
      11. C
      12. peat
      13. ATNO
      15. Ernest
      17. trio
      19. Cr
      21. yam
      22. Br
      23. At
      25. Mao
      26. K
      27. element
      29. Ca
      30. ago
      31. Al
      32. feet

      Down:
      1. escape
      2. larger
      3. cemetery
      4. Ron
      5. one
      9. cape
      11. Co
      13. atom
      14. Na
      16. Siamese
      18. proton
      20. Ra
      22. bang
      24. tea
      25. meat
      29. Cl

II. SECTION TWO

2.1   a. same number
      b. Whatever is necessary to get the electron to move will be given off when the same position is gained. These are opposite (reverse) reactions.

2.2   a. increasing steady attraction
      b. Evidence was given in the vinyl-acetate strip experiment and with magnets.

2.3

20 cm

2.4-2.7 **adult check**

2.8   As the wavelength, λ increases the frequency, υ decreases.

2.9   **adult check**

2.10 a. 3.149
      b. 3.196
      c. 0.159
      d. 0.068
      e. 0.047

2.11 a. As the frequency increases the wavelength decreases (an inverse relationship).
      b. They both show the same inverse relationship.
      c. yes
      d. line spectrum
      e. The spectral results show definite lines, not a continuous rainbow as in the sunlight spectrum.

2.12 The electrons can only fall in specific, definite amounts like stairsteps and therefore have very specific amounts of energy that can be released.

2.13 a. 2
      b. 8
      c. 8

2.14 they are the same

2.15 a. 2
      b. 8
      c. 8

2.16 a. helium
      b. neon
      c. argon

2.17 a. 1
      b. 2

2.18 a. 4
      b. 8

2.19 a. 2
      b. 8
      c. 18
      d. 32
      e. 7
      f. 5
      g. 5
      h. 3

2.20 a. hydrogen, H, 1
      b. helium, He, 2
      c. Lithium, Li, 2, 1
      d. boron, B, 2, 2, 1
      e. neon, Ne, 2, 2, 6
      f. magnesium, Mg, 2, 2, 6, 2
      g. argon, Ar, 2, 2, 6, 2, 6
      h. germanium, Ge, 2, 2, 6, 2, 6, 2, 10, 2

2.21   boron

2.22   a. 1s ⌀ (H)

       b. 2s ⌀ (Li)
           1s ⊗

           2p ⊗ ○ ○
           2s ⊗
       c. 1s ⊗ (C)

           2p ⊗ ⊗ ○
           2s ⊗
       d. 1s ⊗ (O)

       e. 2p ⊗ ⊗ ⊗
           2s ⊗
           1s ⊗ (Ne)

       f. 3s ⊗
           2p ⊗ ⊗ ⊗
           2s ⊗
           1s ⊗ (Mg)

       g. 3p ⊗ ⊗ ○
           3s ⊗
           2p ⊗ ⊗ ⊗
           2s ⊗
           1s ⊗ (S)

       h. 3d ⊗ ⊗ ⊗ ⊗ ⊗
           4s ⊗
           3p ⊗ ⊗ ⊗
           3s ⊗
           2p ⊗ ⊗ ⊗
           2s ⊗
           1s ⊗ (Zn)

       i. 4d ⊗ ⊗ ⊗ ⊗ ⌀
           5s ⊗
           4p ⊗ ⊗ ⊗
           3d ⊗ ⊗ ⊗ ⊗ ⊗
           4s ⊗
           3p ⊗ ⊗ ⊗
           3s ⊗
           2p ⊗ ⊗ ⊗
           2s ⊗ (AG) = 47
           1s ⊗ (Note: $5s^2$, $4d^9$)

2.23   a. flourine; F
          $1s^2 2s^2 2p^5$
       b. neon; Ne
          $1s^2 2s^2 2p^6$
       c. magnesium; Mg
          $1s^2 2s^2 2p^6 3s^2$
       d. phosphorus; P
          $1s^2 2s^2 2p^6 3s^2 3p^3$
       e. sulfur; S
          $1s^2 2s^2 2p^6 3s^2 3p^4$
       f. argon; Ar
          $1s^2 2s^2 2p^6 3s^2 3p^6$
       g. calcium; Ca
          $1s^2 2s^2 2p^6 3s^2 3p^6 4s^2$
       h. zinc; Zn
          $1s^2 2s^2 2p^6 3s^2 3p^6 4s^2 3d^{10}$
       i. selenium; Se
          $1s^2 2s^2 2p^6 3s^2 3p^6 4s^2 3d^{10} 4p^4$
       j. silver; Ag
          $1s^2 2s^2 2p^6 3s^2 3p^6 4s^2 3d^{10} 4p^6 5s^2 4d^9$
       k. barium; Ba
          $1s^2 2s^2 2p^6 3s^2 3p^6 4s^2 3d^{10} 4p^6 5s^2 4d^{10}$
          $5p^6 6s^2$

2.24   third energy level

2.25   p = orbital shape

2.26   4 electrons in the orbital

2.27   boron

2.28   a. The shape is spherical,
           centered on the intersection
           of the x, y, and z axes.
       b. 2
       c. The diagram means that 90
           per cent of the time the s
           electron is located in a
           spherical volume around the
           nucleus.
       d. The nucleus is located in
           the center of the sphere,
           at the intersection of
           the axes.
       e. The three dimensions (axes)
           of the model.

2.29   a. The P_x is shaped like two
           eggs centered on the x-axis.
       b. 2
       c. Ninety percent of the time
           the P_x electrons are
           located within this
           geometric shape.

2.30   a. The P_y looks like 2 eggs
           centered on the y-axis.
       b. 2
       c. Ninety percent of the time
           the P_y electrons are
           located within this geometric
           shape.

2.31   a. The P_z looks like 2 eggs
           centered on the z-axis.
       b. 2
       c. Ninety percent of the time
           the P_z electrons are located
           within the geometric shape.

2.32   The d orbitals describe the 90
       percent probability of finding
       the electrons in certain
       geometric shapes around the
       nucleus. The d_{xy}, d_{xz}, and d_{yz}

       are egg-shaped, 4 lobes each,
       and are found in planes of their
       own, rotated 45^0 to the
       respective axes. The $d_{x^2-y^2}$

       are superimposed over the p_x

and p_y while the d_{z^2} is superimposed over the P_z.

2.33 a. B ⊠ ⊠ ∅ ○ ○
     b. C ⊠ ⊠ ∅ ∅ ○
     c. N ⊠ ⊠ ∅ ∅ ∅
     d. O ⊠ ⊠ ⊠ ∅ ∅
     e. F ⊠ ⊠ ⊠ ⊠ ∅
     f. Ne ⊠ ⊠ ⊠ ⊠ ⊠

2.34 a. yes
     b. The chemical properties of the members of each vertical column are very similar. They react with other elements in similar ratios and similar rates.

2.35 a. $1s^1$; 1
     b. $1s^2\ 2s^1$; 1
     c. $1s^2\ 2s^2\ 2p^3$; 5
     d. $1s^2\ 2s^2\ 2p^5$; 7
     e. $1s^2\ 2s^2\ 2p^6\ 3s^1$; 1
     f. $1s^2\ 2s^2\ 2p^6\ 3s^2$; 2
     g. $1s^2\ 2s^2\ 2p^6\ 3s^2\ 3p^2$; 4
     h. $1s^2\ 2s^2\ 2p^6\ 3s^2\ 3p^4$; 6
     i. $1s^2\ 2s^2\ 2p^2$; 4
     j. $1s^2\ 2s^2\ 2p^6\ 3s^2\ 3p^6$; 0 or 8

2.36 This is an application of the three points detailed prior to this question.
1. Stronger + to - pull, thus making the - harder to remove.
2. Smaller distance between + and -, thus making the - harder to remove.
3. The right side of the dotted line represents an absence of valence electrons and a complete inert gas configuration (Ne) remaining, thus leaving a stable structure that is difficult to disrupt.

2.37 a. 1
     b. 2
     c. 3
     d. $1s^2 2s^2 2p^6$
     e. Ne

2.38 a. +1
     b. +2
     c. +3
     d. +1
     e. +2
     f. +3

2.39 inert gas

2.40 An application of point three listed prior to these activities. The larger atoms have more distance between the + nucleus and the - valence electrons. Therefore, the attraction is decreased and the valence electrons are more easily removed.

2.41 a. Cs
     b. Ba
     c. K
     d. Li
     e. K
     f. Cs
     g. Ba
     h. Al

2.42 a. F
     b. O
     c. Cl
     d. F
     e. F
     f. N
     g. O
     h. N

2.43 a. helium (H)
     b. lithium (Li)
     c. boron (B)
     d. nitrogen (N)
     e. potassium (K)
     f. Nickel (Ni)

2.44 a. 11
     b. 11
     c. 11
     d. 11
     e. yes
     f. They have the same atomic number and atomic number element.
     g. The position of the valence electron in A is $3s^1$ while in B is $5s^1$.

h. B has absorbed some energy from an outside source that caused the $3s^1$ electron to be promoted to the $5s^1$ level.
i. A
j. The valence electron is in its lowest, most stable level.

2.45 **adult check**

2.46 **adult check**

2.47 **adult check**

2.48
a. Be, 4, 4, 9.0, $1s^2 2s^2$, 2
b. C, 6, 6, 12.0, $1s^2 2s^2 2p^2$, 4
c. N, 7, 7, 14.0, $1s^2 2s^2 2p^3$, 5
d. Na, 11, 11, 23.0, $1s^2 2s^2 2p^6 3s^1$, 1
e. Al, 13, 13, 27.0, $1s^2 2s^2 2p^6 3s^2 3p^1$, 3
f. Cl, 17, 17, 35.5, $1s^2 2s^2 2p^6 3s^2 3p^5$, 7
g. Sc, 21, 21, 45.0, $Rr + 4s^2 3d^1$, 3
h. Ni, 28, 28, 58.7, $Rr + 4s^2 3d^8$, 10
i. Kr, 36, 36, 83.8, $Ar + 4s^2 3d^{10} 4p^6$, 0
j. Te, 52, 52, 127.9, $Kr + 5s^2 4d^{10} 5p^4$, 16 or 6

2.49 **adult check**

2.50 Across:
1. aluminum
5. shell
8. Si
9. Ca
10. Bi
11. He
12. Mo
13. liquids
17. metric
19. Planck
22. outer
23. Ar
24. Ra
26. metal
28. oxygen
32. Os
33. K
34. Ge
35. octet
37. N
39. let
40. top
42. neon

Across:
44. liter
47. Sr
48. ten
49. also
50. Bohr
52. atoms
54. period
57. La
58. ion
59. Co
60. family
61. nucleus
Down:
2. Lee
3. isotope
4. Ni
5. sail
6. Lb
7. Li
9. cup
11. hydrogen
12. me
13. lit
14. ice
15. Dalton
16. Sn
17. Mg
18. Ru
20. cal
21. Kr
25. axe
26. meter
27. As
29. gain
30. noble
31. At
36. electron
38. loss
41. protons
43. odor
45. in
46. gas
48. troll
50. beta
51. hi
53. ml
55. day
56. doe
59. Cl

III. SECTION THREE

3.1 **adult check**

3.2 **adult check**

3.3 The same pattern is repeated starting with the column IA elements as having the greatest volume, then decreasing as the center of the period is approached, then increasing again as the period ends.

3.4 Again, there is a very regular repeating pattern evident from the graph, ending each period with a high value for the inert gases.

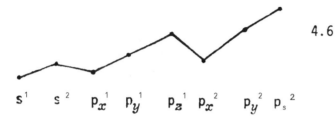

$s^1 \quad s^2 \quad p_x^1 \quad p_y^1 \quad p_z^1 \quad p_x^2 \quad p_y^2 \quad p_s^2$

3.5 teacher check

3.6 The repeating or recurring chemical and physical properties that form the Periodic Law are based on the repeating nature of the valence electron configurations. Vertical columns have similar chemical and physical properties because they have the same valence electron structure.

IV. SECTION FOUR

4.1 a. $^{230}_{90}Th$

 b. $^{4}_{2}He$

 c. $^{248}_{96}Cm$

 d. $^{218}_{84}Po$

 e. $^{238}_{94}Pu$

 f. $^{4}_{2}He$; $^{0}_{-1}e$

4.2 **adult check**

4.3 The chemical properties of all members of a vertical column are similar.

4.4 a. IIA
 b. IIA
 c. yes
 d. The same thing should occur because they are so chemically similar.

4.5 The $^{90}_{38}Sr$ would substitute for the Ca and the milk produced by the cows would contain Sr-90, a radioactive substance. The radioactive Sr-90 would then settle in bones and teeth of humans.

4.6 The substitution of Sr-90 for Ca caused the bones of the radioactive milk drinkers to take on a high concentration of radioactivity. The high radioactivity caused the red blood cells to reproduce abnormally in the bones and caused anemia in children.

4.7 **adult check**

1.1   0.0001 moles/ml

1.2   0.0002 moles

1.3   a. 0.000001 moles
       b. 1/200 = 0.5%

1.4   0.0002 moles

1.5   0.0002 moles

1.6   2:3

1.7   1:1:1

1.8   a. 1, 1, 1, 1
       b. 1, 2, 2, 1
       c. 1, 3, 3, 1

1.9   a. II A
       b. III A
       c. VII A
       d. VIII A
       e. 1
       f. 3
       g. 7
       h. 8
       i. 1
       j. 2
       k. 3
       l. 8

1.10   a. inert gas VIII A
       b. 8
       c. The s-p sublevels are completely
          filled.

1.11   The magnesium would rather lose
       two electrons than gain six.

1.12   The aluminum would rather lose
       three electrons than gain five.

1.13   The chlorine would rather gain one
       electron than lose seven.

1.14   a. $1s^2\ 2s^2$
       b. $1s^2$
       c. +2

1.15   a. $1s^2\ 2s^2\ 2p^6\ 3s^2\ 3p^5$
       b. $1s^2\ 2s^2\ 2p^6\ 3s^2\ 3p^6$
       c. -1

1.16   a. $1s^2\ 2s^2\ 2p^6\ 3s^1$
       b. $1s^2\ 2s^2\ 2p^6$
       c. +1

1.17   a. $1s^2\ 2s^2\ 2p^5$
       b. $1s^2\ 2s^2\ 2p^6$
       c. -1

1.18   a. $1s^2\ 2s^2\ 2p^4$
       b. $1s^2\ 2s^2\ 2p^6$
       c. -2

1.19   a. $1s^2\ 2s^2\ 2p^6\ 3s^2$
       b. $1s^2\ 2s^2\ 2p^6$
       c. +2

1.20   a. $1s^2\ 2s^2\ 2p^6\ 3s^2\ 3p^6\ 4s^2$
       b. $1s^2\ 2s^2\ 2p^6\ 3s^2\ 3p^6$
       c. +2

1.21   a. $1s^2\ 2s^2\ 2p^1$
       b. $1s^2$
       c. +3

1.22   a. $1s^2\ 2s^2\ 2p^6\ 3s^2\ 3p^3$
       b. $1s^2\ 2s^2\ 2p^6\ 3s^2\ 3p^6$
       c. -3

1.23   a. $1s^2\ 2s^2\ 2s^6\ 3s^2\ 3p^4$
       b. $1s^2\ 2s^2\ 2p^6\ 3s^2\ 3p^6$
       c. -2

1.24   a. $1s^2\ 2s^2\ 2p^6\ 3s^2\ 3p^1$
       b. $1s^2\ 2s^2\ 2p^6$
       c. +3

1.25   a. $1s^2\ 2s^2\ 2p^3$
       b. $1s^2\ 2s^2\ 2p^6$
       c. -3

1.26   a. $1s^2\ 2s^2\ 2p^6\ 3s^2\ 3p^2$
       b. $1s^2\ 2s^2\ 2p^6$ or $3s^2\ 3p^6$
       c. ±4

1.27   a. $1s^2\ 2s^2\ 2p^2$
       b. $1s^2\ 2s^2\ 2p^6$ or $1s^2$
       c. ±4

1.28 All ions of the same charge are found in the same family (column).

1.29
a. +1
b. 1
c. +2
d. 2
e. +3
f. 3
g. +4
h. 4
i. -3
j. 5
k. -2
l. 6
m. -1
n. 7
o. 0
p. 8 or 0

1.30
a. DE_2
b. DG
c. NO
d. Both ions are positive and positive charges repel, so no bond could form between A^{+1} and D^{+2}

1.31 KBr

1.32 NaCl

1.33 $CaCl_2$

1.34 LiF

1.35 Cs_2S

1.36 $SrBr_2$

1.37 MgO

1.38 BeS

1.39 RbCl

1.40 BaO

1.41 $AlCl_3$

1.42 Al_2O_3

1.43 $MgCl_2$

1.44
a. metals
b. nonmetals

c. The positive ions (metals) tend to be on the left and the negative tend to be on the right (nonmetals).

1.45
a. MgS
b. AlI_3
c. Ce_2O
d. PI_3
e. H_2O
f. CCl_4
g. SiO_2
h. Al_2O_3

1.46
a. Na_2CO_3
b. $Ca_3(PO_4)_2$
c. H_2S
d. $KMnO_4$
e. $CaCO_3$
f. $Al(NO_3)_3$
g. $(NH_4)_2Cr_2O_7$
h. $BaSO_4$
i. Li_2CrO_4
j. $Mg(CH_3COO)_2$
k. $(NH_4)_2CO_3$
l. SrS

1.47
a. $Ca_3(PO_4)_2 + \underline{5}\ C + 3SiO_2 \rightarrow \underline{3}\ CaSiO_3 + \underline{2}\ P + \underline{5}\ CO$
b. $\underline{4}\ P + \underline{5}\ O_2 \rightarrow 2P_2O_5$
c. $\underline{2}\ As_2S_3 + 9\ O_2 \rightarrow 2As_2O_3 + \underline{6}\ SO_2$
d. $CS_2 + \underline{3}\ Cl_2 \rightarrow CCl_4 + S_2Cl_2$
e. $\underline{2}\ Na_2CO_3 + CaCO_3 + 6\ SiO_2 \rightarrow Na_4CaSi_6O_{15} + \underline{3}\ CO_2$
f. $\underline{2}\ C_8H_{18} + 25\ O_2 \rightarrow 16\ CO_2 + \underline{18}\ H_2O$
g. $2CH_3OH + \underline{3}\ O_2 \rightarrow 2CO_2 + \underline{4}\ H_2O$
h. $2C_2H_2 + \underline{5}\ O_2 \rightarrow 4CO_2 + \underline{2}\ H_2O$

II. SECTION TWO

2.1
a. 1.0 cm
b. 1.2 cm
c. 1.5 cm

2.2 bromine

2.3 decrease

2.4 bromine

2.5 Since the F is smaller in size than Br, the nucleus of Br is further from the hydrogen electron. Because of the increased distance between Br-H, the attraction is less and a weaker bond is formed.

2.6   a. metals
       b. nonmetals
       c. inert gases

2.7

								Inert Gases
H 2.1								He 0
Li 1.0	Be 1.5	Metals	B 2.0	C 2.5	N 3.0	O 3.5	F 4.0	Ne 0
Na 0.9	Mg 1.2		Al 1.5	Si 1.8	P 2.1	S 2.5	Cl 3.0	Ar 0
K 0.8	Ca 1.0			As 2.0			Br 2.8	Kr 0
Rb 0.8	Sr 1.0						I 2.5	Xe 0
Cs 0.7	Ba 0.9							

Nonmetals

Figure 2

2.8   The relationships of ionization energy and electronegativity are directly related. As one value increases, so does the other.

2.9   Opposite electrical charges attract each other. Therefore, an ionic bond is held together because a positive ion and a negative ion are attracted to each other.

2.10   As the difference increases, so does the amount of ionic character.

2.11   ionic

2.12   a. 1.6-1.7
       b. 22%
       c. covalent

2.13   a. NaCl
       b. KCl

2.14   a. N_2
       b. O_2
       c. H_2

2.15   increases

2.16   a. 67
       b. s
       c. 94
       d. s
       e. 55
       f. s
       g. 30
       h. l
       i. 22
       j. g
       k. 39
       l. 1

m. 0
n. g
o. 6
p. g
q. 43
r. 1

2.17   a. The greater the ionic character, the greater the tendency to be a solid.
       b. The greater the ionic character, the greater the bond strength.
       c. The more ionic the bond, the higher will be the M.P. and B.P. of the compound.

2.18   a. ionic
       b. FrF or CsF
       c. Because the compounds have the greatest electronegativity value differences.

2.19   a. no
       b. Because every element has some attraction for its valence electron, no bond can cause a 100% separation of the valence electron from one atom to another.

2.20   The columns furthest from each other (I and VII) will have the greatest electronegativity value difference.

2.21   1. metals
       2. nonmetals
       3. inert gases

2.22   a. inert gases (3)
       b. metals (1)
       c. metals (1)

2.23   Metals have very nondirected bonding electrons. This nondirected nature allows the electrons to flow easily from one atom to another in a metallic substance. The electrons are not "tied down" to any one location in the solid. Therefore electricity and heat can easily "flow" or be conducted in the metal.

2.24   a. ionic
       b. metallic
       c. covalent
       d. ionic
       e. covalent
       f. covalent
       g. covalent
       h. covalent

3.1 The stream of water was bent toward the strip.

3.2 Most students will predict that the stream will be repelled by the vinyl strip.

3.3 a. depends
b. Look for logic and soundness of reasoning.

3.4 a. 39%
b. covalent

3.5 a. 6%
b. covalent

3.6 a. Hint:
Most students will say the same as for water.
b. Hint:
Most students will say the same as for water.
c. Hint:
Look for logic and reasonableness.

3.7 depends on prediction

3.8 Hint:
Look for reasonableness of answer.

3.9

s	s^2p	s^2p^2	s^2p^4	s^2p^5	s^2p^6
000	∅00	∅∅0	⊠∅∅	⊠⊠∅	⊠⊠⊠
∅	⊠	⊠	⊠	⊠	⊠
1	3	4	6	7	8
0	1	1	2	3	
1	1	2	2	1	

3.10 1

3.11 2

3.12 2

3.13 The II A elements must unpair the valence electrons to produce two singles.

3.14 a. 3
b. 1

3.15 Because there are two p and one s orbitals involved in the hybrid formation.

3.16 The pair of s electrons unpairs and with the two singles produces the four electrons for the four bonds.

3.17 sp^3

3.18

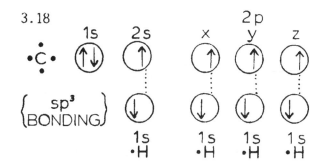

3.19 **After the sp^3, there is no open orbital available for the unpaired electron to go. There are only 3p orbitals and each has one electron as there is no room to promote one from the s^2.**

3.20

2	3	3	2	1	0
sp	sp^2	none	none	none	none
		or	or	or	
		p^3	p^2	p	

3.21 Because 2p electrons are available for bonding.

3.22

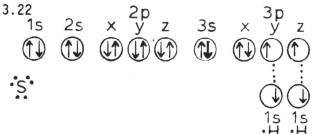

3.23 The diagram shows the bonding of the one hydrogen electron (↓) with the single unpaired valence electron of fluorine (↑). The arrows are opposite (opposite magnetic spins).

3.24 a. HF
b. HX

3.25 In order to bond, there must be unpaired single electrons available to bond with another atom. The inert gases have complete s-p orbitals which leave no electrons unpaired to bond.

3.26 Hint:
Look for depth, accuracy, and presentation.

3.27 Shape should be linear.

3.28 Shape should be all three atoms in a straight line (linear).

3.29 Shape should be planar, triangular with the angles being 120^0 each.

3.30 Shape should be planar, triangular with the angles being 120^0 each.

3.31 Hint:
Should describe a tetrahedral shape with the angles being about 109^0 each.

3.32 Hint:
Should describe a tetrahedral shape with the angles being about 109^0 each.

3.33 The similarities should be that the basic structure is still tetrahedral but that the angle is less as more electron pairs are present.

3.34 Hint:
Look for depth of answer and specific points. The *p* orbital is linear while the sp^3 is tetrahedral. Inert gases have all orbitals filled and are pyramid shaped.

3.37 a. yes
b. The pull toward Cl (3.0) is greater than toward hydrogen (2.1). Therefore the molecule is polar with the H as δ^+ and the Cl as δ^-. (The more electronegative element will have δ^- since it attracts e^-.)

3.38 Basis should be that H_2O is polar and CCl_4 is nonpolar.

3.39 a. S, H H
b. bent
c. polar

3.40 a. Cl—Al—Cl, Cl
b. planar triangular
c. nonpolar

3.41 a. H-F
b. linear
c. polar

3.42 a. Cl Cl C H H
b. tetrahedral
c. polar

3.43 a. Cl Cl Sn Cl Cl
b. tetrahedral
c. nonpolar

3.44 a. Cl Te Cl
b. bent
c. polar

3.35

LiH	BeH₂	BH₃	CH₄		H₂O	HF	none
Li-H	H-Be-H	H H B H	H H C H H		O H H	H-F	0
Li×H	H×Be×H	H ·x B× H× H	H× ×H C× H× H		·O· × × H H	H×F:	none
	Linear	Planar Triangular	tetra hedral		bent	linear	

3.36

polar	nonpolar	nonpolar	nonpolar	polar	polar	polar	none

3.45   a. linear
       b. linear
       c. planar, triangular
       d. tetrahedral
       e. pyramidal
       f. bent
       g. linear
       h. none

3.46   a.

       b. FxNxF
          ·x
          F
       c. pyramidal
       d. polar

3.47   a. F-F
       b. :F:F:
       c. linear
       d. nonpolar

3.48   a.

       b. :FxOx
           :F:
       c. bent
       d. polar

3.49   a. Li-F
       b. LixF:
       c. linear
       d. polar

3.50   a. F-Be-F
       b. :Fx Be x F:
       c. linear
       d. nonpolar

3.51   a.

       b.

       c. planar, triangular
       d. nonpolar

3.52   a.

       b. :Fx xF:
           C
        ·x x·
       :F: :F:
       c. tetrahedral
       d. nonpolar

1.1   NaCl - clear, colorless solution
      (liquid)
      K_2CrO_4 - clear, yellow solution
      $AgNO_3$ - clear, colorless solution

1.2   A cloudy rust-colored solid forms with
      the $AgNO_3/K_2CrO_4$ and a cloudy white
      solid forms with the $AgNO_3/NaCl$.

1.3   Example:
      There was a definite change in
      appearance; the liquids produced
      a solid.

1.4   As the NaCl was added, the rusty-
      colored solid dissolved and was
      replaced by a white solid.

1.5   Example:
      The rusty solid was eaten by the
      NaCl and a new solid was formed.

1.6 $FeSO_4$ - straw yellow color, clear
      solution
      $KMnO_4$ - deep purple solution

1.7   The color of the $KMnO_4$ changed
      quickly when the $FeSO_4$ was added.
      The resulting solution was straw
      yellow.

1.8   Example:
      There was an obvious color change
      in one of the reactants.

1.9   NaCl - clear, colorless solution
      NH_4NO_3 - clear, colorless solution

1.10 No apparent (visible) change took
      place.

1.11 There is no outward appearance of
      a chemical change.

1.12 The solutions are all clear, color-
      less solutions. The $CaCO_3$ is a
      white solid.

1.13 a. A vigorous reaction takes
         place with a gas released.
      b. A small reaction takes place
         with a gas released.
      c. **A moderate reaction takes place
         with a gas released.**
      d. A slow reaction takes place
         with a gas produced.
      e. Little or no evidence of a
         reaction is seen.

1.14 The solid and liquid react, form-
      ing a gas. A change of state is
      evident.

1.15 a. A solid was formed from two
         liquids (change of state).
      b. A color change was seen in one
         or more reactants.
      c. A gas was formed from a solid-
         liquid mixture (change of
         state).

1.16 The HCl is a colorless (slightly
      yellow) liquid solution. It has
      a very strong, sharp odor.

1.17 No visible change took place but
      the temperature went up about 3^0C.

1.18 There was a rise in the tempera-
      ture, indicating a reaction
      (energy change).

1.19 a. yes
      b. yes
      c. cool
      d. release
      e. less

1.20 NaOH - white solid, chunky; gets
      shiny as it is open to the air.

1.21 The solid dissolves in the water
      and the temperature rises about
      3^0C. The resulting solution is
      cloudy to almost colorless.

1.22 The solid dissolved and the
      temperature rose, indicating a
      reaction occurred.

1.23   a. yes
         b. yes
         c. take away
         d. same
         e. reactants
         f. yes

1.24 E_2 + heat

1.25   All three solutions are colorless.

1.26   When the indicator was added to the NaOH solution, the liquids turned a bright purple (crimson). As the HCl was added, suddenly the solution turned colorless. As the HCl was added the temperature rose about 2^0C.

1.27   There was a color change and a temperature change. Both indicate that a reaction has taken place.

1.28   a. yes
         b. the temperature increased

1.29   a. yes
         b. reactants

1.30 $E_1 \rightarrow E_2$ + heat

1.31   a. decreases
         b. add
         c. products
         d. no

1.32   **a. decreased (-)**
         b. +
         c. The reactions are opposite. The exothermic reaction loses energy (-) and the endothermic reaction gains energy (+).

1.33 E_1 + heat $\rightarrow E_2$ or $E_1 \rightarrow E_2$ - heat

1.34   Any order:
         a. solid (precipitate) formation
         b. color change
         c. gas formation
         d. temperature change

1.35   exothermic

1.36   endothermic

1.37   Any order:
         b, c, e

1.38   a. yes
         b. Apparently the energy contained in $C_{(diamond)}$ is greater than that contained in $C_{(graphite)}$

1.39
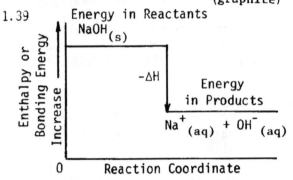

1.40
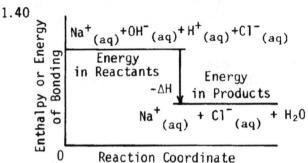

1.41
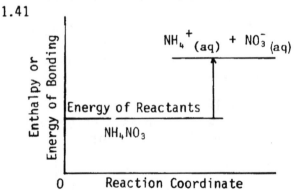

1.42   a. lost
         b. bond energy
         c. 104
         d. 1.73×10^{-22}

1.43   a. 1, 2, 1, 2
         b.   H   0-0

              H$\diagup \!\!\!\!\! \overset{C}{\underset{|}{H}} \!\!\!\!\! \diagdown$H

               H   0-0

1.44   a. C-H   99
         b. C-H   99
         c. C-H   99
         d. C-H   99
         e. 0-0   119
         f. 0-0   119
         g. 634

1.45   O = C = O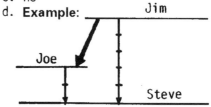

a. C = O   -192
b. C = O   -192
c. H - O   -111
d. H - O   -111
e. H - O   -111
f. H - O   -111
g. -828

1.46   +634 + (-828) = -194 kcal

1.47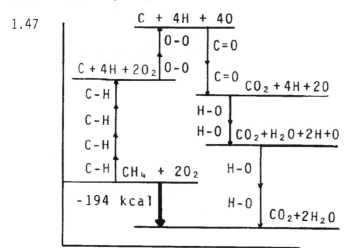

1.48   a. -194 kcal
        b. lost
        c. released to

1.49   a. You may be able to use the graph to predict the ΔH for some reactions.
        b. Use the values from the Enthalpy Graph for CO_2 and H_2O
        $\Delta H = -96_{CO_2} + 2(-68_{H_2O}) = -232$ kcal
        (This is very close to the experimental value: -194 kcal

1.50   a. the ΔH should still be -194 kcal
        b. Generalization: The ΔH for a reaction does not depend on the mechanism.

1.51   a. hopefully, yes
        b. -194 (should be)
        c. -194 (should be)
        d. The route does not make any difference. The ΔH is always the same for the same reaction.

1.52   a. **3 floors**
        b. unknown
        c. no
        d. **Example:**

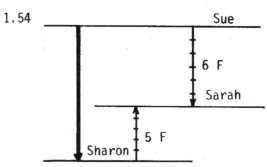

1.53

1.54

1.55

1.56   a. -94.05 kcal
        b. -67.6 kcal
        c. -26.45 kcal
        d. -13.5 kcal
        e. +8.1 kcal
        f. +21.6 kcal
        g. Generalization: ΔH's like bond energies are additive. This conclusion agrees with previous predictions. The diagrams for 1.51 and 1.55 show that ΔH is independent of the path you follow from reactants to products.
        h. They should be the same.

1.57 $(\frac{1}{3})(57.8 \text{ kcal}) = 19.3 \text{ kcal}$

1.58 $(\frac{12.5\,g}{28\,g})(-331.6 \text{ kcal}) = -148. \text{ kcal}$

II. SECTION TWO

2.1   10g/hr

2.2   a. more
      b. about 2 times
      c. increased

2.3   a. less
      b. about ½
      c. decreased
      d. increase
      e. The greater the concentration (crowdedness), the greater the chance of a collision occurring between two substances.

2.4   a. 1.0 M
      b. 1.0 M
      c. Because 1.0 M is ten times as strong (concentrated) as 0.1 M.
      d. 1.0 M
      e. Because the 1. 0 M is ten times as concentrated, yielding ten times the collisions, which potentially would increase the probability of a reaction by a factor of ten.

2.5   Example data:
      a. 0.5 minutes
      b. 0.75 minutes
      c. 1.25 minutes
      d. 4 minutes
      e. 10 minutes

2.6   **adult check**

2.7   a. increase
      b. increase
      c. they should agree
      d. As the concentration of reactants increases, the rate of the reaction increases.

2.8   Because the probability (chance) of the reactants colliding successfully is increased if they are more concentrated (crowded), they will react at a more rapid rate.

2.9   a. increased
      b. increased

2.10   a. vigorous shake
      b. vigorous shake
      c. vigorous
      d. moderate
      e. gentle

2.11   a. cool
      b. warm
      c. hot
      d. The more energy the reactants have, the faster they move and the greater their chance to hit each other.

2.12   Example data:
      a. $2^{\circ}C$ 8.25 minutes
      b. $23^{\circ}C$ 3.75 minutes
      c. $50^{\circ}C$ 1.25 minutes
      d. $75^{\circ}C$ 0.60 minutes
      e. $98^{\circ}C$ 0.25 minutes

2.13   **adult check**

2.14   a. it should agree
      b. increase
      c. As the speed of the molecules (reactants) increases, the number of collisions/second increases and, therefore, increases the chances of the reactants colliding to react. **Also, the hotter the reactants, the more collisions have the necessary energy to actually react.**

2.15   Example:

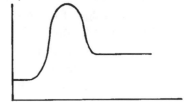

2.16   a. If you double the pressure, the volume is halved. Therefore, the concentration is doubled and the reaction rate should increase.
      b. If the number of molecules of A is doubled, the concentration is doubled and this increases the probability of a collision. This increased probability increases the reaction rate.

c. If the temperature is decreased, the kinetic energy (speed) is decreased which causes less collisions and lowers the rate of reaction.

2.17 a. exothermic
b. The high pressures and temperatures are economically unacceptable.
c. ΔH = -12.000 kcal/mole
d. 1.70 grams NH_3 = 0.10 mole

$$\frac{N_2}{NH_3} = \frac{1}{2} = \frac{x}{0.10}$$

x = 0.05 moles
(0.05 moles)(28g/mole) = 1.4 g

2.18 a.

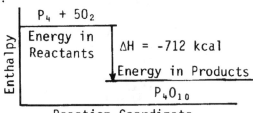

b. 124 g/mole
12.4 g = 0.1 mole
0.1 mole P_4 produces
71.2 kcal of heat

2.19 a. endothermic
b. 43.8 kcal
c. products

2.20 a. slow
b. Because the reaction is endothermic and the activation energy is high, the reaction rate will be slow.

2.21 Example data:
a. 0 ml
b. 50 ml

2.22 a. The rate is increased when the liver is added.
b. no
c. high
d. Since the reaction went easily with the liver and nothing

occurred without it, the activation energy must have been high, preventing a reaction at room temperature.

2.23 a. yes
b. A catalyst reacts with the reactants in such a way as to increase or decrease the activation energy necessary for the reaction to occur.

2.24 **adult check**

2.25 a.

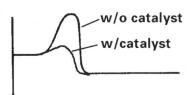

b. Since the liver catalyzes the decomposition of H_2O_2, the activation energy level must be lowered.

2.26 Ideal conditions include: high concentration, high temperature, and a positive catalyst. (Student should include collision theory for each factor).

III. SECTION THREE

3.1 a. 2
b. 4
c. 5
d. 7

3.2 The number increased as the voltage (energy) increased.

3.3 a. 10
b. 12
c. 11
d. 13
e. 11
f. Average =11.4

3.4 The number remained about the same for all five trials.

3.5 a. 16
b. 17
c. 16
d. 18
e. 15

f. 16.4

3.6 The average increased.

3.7 The actual number above the line remains nearly constant for the five trials.

3.8
a. 22
b. 24
c. 22
d. 23
e. 22
f. 22.6

3.9 increased

3.10 remained nearly constant

3.11 the same

3.12 they are different

3.13 remain about the same

3.14
a. Fe^{+3}
b. NO_3^-
c. K^+
d. SCN^-

3.15
a. Examples:
$(Fe)(SCN)_3$, KNO_3
b. The KNO_3 is a colorless solution.

3.16
a. increased
b. greater
c. Some Fe^{+3} were left unreacted.

3.17
a. increased
b. increased
c. Some SCN^- were left unreacted.

3.18
a. $FeSCN^{+2}$
b. Na^+, HPO_4^{-2}
c. Examples:
$FeSCNHPO_4$, $FeHPO_4^{+1}$, $NaSCN$

3.19
a. yes
b. more
c. yes
d. liquid
e. gaseous
f. yes

3.20
a. $\dfrac{[NaHSO_4]}{[Na^+][H^+][SO_4^{-2}]}$

b. $\dfrac{[H_2SO_4]}{[H^+][H^+][SO_4^{-2}]}$

c. $\dfrac{[H_2SO_4]}{[H^+]^2[SO_4^{-2}]}$

d. $\dfrac{[CH_3OH]}{[CO][H_2]^2}$

3.21
a. $\dfrac{[NO_2]^2}{[N_2O_4]}$
b. 10

3.22
a. $\dfrac{[H_2S]^2}{[H_2]^2[S_2]}$
b. 9.38×10^5
c. products

3.23
a. small
b. $\dfrac{[H_2]^2[O_2]}{[H_2O]^2}$

3.24 Optional:

$$\frac{[Cl_2][PCl_3]}{[PCl_5]} = 2.24 \times 10^{-2}$$

$$= \frac{[x][0.174]}{[0.235]}$$

$$x = \frac{(0.0224)(0.235)}{(0.174)}$$
$$= [0.0303]$$
$$= 3.03 \times 10^{-2} \text{ moles/liter}$$

3.25
a. smaller
b. products
c. products

3.26 A small Keq means that the reactants are favored and the mixture is largely reactants. The smaller the Keq, the less product is produced. The equilibrium is far to the left.

3.27
a. increased
b. increased
c. yes
d. increase
e. yes
f. decrease

3.28   Since the added Fe^{+3} caused an increase in the $[Fe^{+3}]$, the probability of the Fe^{+3} reacting with SCN^- increased. This increased reaction rate decreased the $[Fe^{+3}]$ and $[SCN^-]$, but resulted in an increased $[FeSCN^{+2}]$.

3.29   When an equilibrium is upset by the addition of one or more reactants or products, the reaction will attempt to regain the original equilibrium condition. As a result a compromise will be achieved such that the equilibrium moves toward the original position but never regains it. The side of the equilibrium not getting the addition will increase in concentration and the chemicals on the same side as the increase will decrease in concentration.

3.30   a. endothermic
        b.

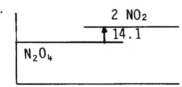

        c. $\Delta H = +14.1$ kcal/mole N_2O_4

3.31   a. **adult check**
        b. decrease
        c. products
        d. yes

3.32   a. increased
        b. The system will be driven to the side with least molecules (pressure).

3.33   a. decrease
        b. increase
        c. increases
        d. decrease
        e. decreased
        f. decrease
        g. **adult check**
        h. An increase in pressure will cause the equilibrium to be shifted in favor of the least pressure side (least number of molecules) in this reaction.

3.34   Optional:
        The wire and weights will cut through the ice and the ice will refreeze after the cut has been made. The added pressure causes the ice to melt. When the pressure is released the water refreezes. Sharp skates means you are really skating on a film of water which serves as a lubricant.

3.35   Optional:
        adult check

3.36   Optional:
        adult check

3.37   Optional:
        adult check

3.38   Optional:
        a. An increased pressure will force the equilibrium to the side with the least number of molecules, the product side.
        b. An increased $[O_2]$ will cause the $[SO_3]$ to increase and the $[SO_2]$ to decrease in the process of achieving the compromise state.
        c. An increased volume will in effect decrease the pressure. A decrease in pressure will favor the reactants (opposite to a).
        d. A platinum catalyst will not affect the equilibrium once it is reached. A catalyst only affects that rate at which equilibrium is reached.
        e. An increased temperature will favor the endothermic side, the reactants. The equilibrium will shift to the left.

3.39   Optional:
        a. $\dfrac{[Al^{+3}][Cl^-]^3}{[AlCl_3]}$

        b. $\dfrac{[NO]^4[H_2O]^6}{[NH_3]^4[O_2]^5}$

        c. $\dfrac{[FeS][H^+]^2}{[Fe^{+2}][H_2S]}$

1.1	23.0	
1.2	1.0	
1.3	16.0	
1.4	18.0	
1.5	12.0	
1.6	44.0	
1.7	84.0	
1.8	62.0	
1.9	28.0	

1.10 a. $N_2 + \textcircled{3} H_2 \rightleftharpoons \textcircled{2} NH_3$
       b. $\textcircled{3} Fe + \textcircled{4} H_2O \rightleftharpoons Fe_3O_4 + \textcircled{4} H_2$

1.11 a. One mole (atom) of Fe plus one mole (atom) of S produces one mole (molecule) of FeS.
       b. Two moles (molecules) of $KClO_3$ break up to produce two moles (molecules) of KCl and three moles (molecules) of O_2.
       c. One mole (molecule) of CH_4 plus two moles (molecules) of O_2 produce one mole (molecule) of CO_2 and two moles (molecules) of H_2O.

1.12 a. H_2, O_2
           H_2O
       b. HgO
           Hg, O_2

1.13 a. $2 H_2O \rightarrow 2 H_2 + O_2$
       b. $2 HCl + Zn \rightarrow ZnCl_2 + H_2$
       c. $2 H_2O_2 \rightarrow 2 H_2O + O_2$
       d. $2 H_2 + CO \rightarrow CH_3OH$
       e. $3 Fe + 2 O_2 \rightarrow Fe_3O_4$
       f. $4 Al + 3 O_2 \rightarrow 2 Al_2O_3$
       g. $3 NH_4OH + AlCl_3 \rightarrow Al(OH)_3 + 3 NH_4Cl$

1.14 true

1.15 false

1.16 false

1.17 true

1.18 true

1.19 true

1.20 a. 0.1
       b. 5.85

1.21 a. 0.5
       b. 0.5
       c. 29.2
       d. 0.292

1.22 a. less
       b. decreased
       c. remained the same
       d. no
       e. no
       f. yes

1.23 a. 0.05
       b. 0.005, 0.005
       c. 0.292, 0.292

1.24 a. 50
       b. 0.002, 0.002
       c. 0.117, 0.117

1.25 a. 5.0ml-M
       b. 100, 0.05, 5.0ml-M
       c. The two values are the same.
       d. 10ml x 0.2M = 50ml x 0.04M

1.26 a. $4.32 \times 10^2 \div 20.0 = 21.6M$
       b. $0.5 \div 0.25 = 2.0 M$
       c. $\frac{100}{342} \div 1.15 = 0.25 M$
       d. $0.1 \div 2 = 0.05 M$

1.27 e

1.23 c

1.29 c, e, h, j, l

1.30   a. ionic (67% ionic)
           b. covalent (6% ionic)
           c. covalent (39% ionic)
           d. covalent (39% ionic)
           e. covalent (4% ionic)(39% ionic)
           f. ionic (70% ionic))
           g. covalent (19% ionic)

1.31   a. ionic
           b. ionic
           c. dissociate
           d. ionize
           e. covalent
           f. increases

1.32   Complete for each Test
           a. yes, no
           b. yes, yes
           c. yes, yes
           d. yes, no
           e. yes, no
           f. yes, no
           g. yes, no
           h. yes, yes
           i. yes, no
           j. yes, no
           k. yes, yes
           l. yes, no
           m. yes, yes
           n. yes, yes

1.33   a. yes
           b. yes
           c. no
           d. Example:
                Molecules that have similar
                polarity properties dissolve
                in each other, but dissimilar
                molecules do not dissolve.
           e. Example:
                Because grease is nonpolar
                and is more like CCl_4 than
                H_2O it dissolves in CCl_4 but
                not in H_2O.
           f. Example:
                Because both HCl and H_2O are
                polar, the H_2O has more
                "power" to pull the HCl apart.

1.34   a. yes
           b. yes

1.35

1.36   a. yes
           b. decrease and then increases
           c. decrease, then increase
           d. Example:
                The meter reading decreased
                and then increased.
           e. Apparently as the reaction
                occurred the number of ions
                decreased.
           f. $Ba^{+2} + 2OH^-$ and $2H^+ + SO_4^{-2} \rightarrow$
                $BaSO_4\downarrow + 2H_2O$
           g. equal
           h. Example:
                At the low point all the ions
                are tied up in the precipi-
                tate, $BaSO_4$, and water, H_2O.
                Neither of the products con-
                duct electricity.
           i. Example:
                Both before and after the
                equivalence point, unreacted
                ions are available to carry
                the current.

1.37   a. 2
           b. 2
           c. 3
           d. 4
           e. 3
           f. 2
           g. 2
           h. 5

1.38   a. $(NH_4)_2CO_3$
           b. PbI_2
           c. H_2SO_4
           d. $Ca(OH)_2$
           e. $NaOH$
           f. ZnC_2O_4
           g. $Sn(SO_4)_2$
           h. $AgNO_3$

1.39   a. 3
           b. 3
           c. 3
           d. 3
           e. 2
           f. 2
           g. 3
           h. 2

II. SECTION TWO

2.1   Either order:
        a. dissolving (separation)
        b. diffusion

2.2   solute

2.3   diffusion

2.4   equilibrium

2.5   away from

2.6   a. the crystal dissolves completely
        b. part of the crystal dissolves
        c. no change is seen in the crystal size

2.7   water

2.8   The salt is most like the water (polar solvents dissolve ionic crystals).

2.9   Example:
The solvent affects the dissolving process because the dissolving process involves the intermingling of solvent and solute. If the two are unlike each other the dissolving process is resisted.

2.10   Example:
        a. 5 minutes
        b. 30 seconds

2.11   Example:
Because of the increased surface area of the pulverized over the crystal, the dissolving process can take place on many more solute particles at the same time.

2.12   Example:
        a. 5 minutes
        b. 1.5 minutes

2.13   Example:
Since the dissolving process uses energy, the system with the greatest energy available will dissolve first. Both the dissociation and diffusion steps occur more capably.

2.14   Example:
        a. 2 minutes
        b. 6 minutes

2.15   Example:
The stirring speeds up the diffusion process and brings fresh solvent in contact with the solute crystals.

2.16   Any order:
        a. pulverize the solute
        b. heat the solvent
        c. stir the solvent

2.17   a. 2
         b. 2

2.18   a. 0.31 g
         b. 0.0115
         c. 3.34 g
         d. 0.0161

2.19   a. moles per liter
         b. concentration

2.20   0.161 M

2.21   0.322 M

2.22   a.   3
       b. $\dfrac{Al}{Pb} = \dfrac{2}{3} = \dfrac{0.0115}{x}$
            $2x = (3)(0.0115)$

       0.0173 moles Pb to form

2.23   0.173 M

2.24   0.346 M

2.25   a.   4.42 g
       b.   0.0159
       c.   0.159 M
       d.   0.318 M

2.26   a. $[0.161][0.322]^2 = 0.01669$
       b. $[0.173][0.346]^2 = 0.02071$
       c. $[0.159][0.318]^2 = 0.01608$

2.27   a.   the temperatures for the K_{sp} may be different than the standard
       b.   impurities on the $PbCl_2$ and/or the Al wire cause errors
       c.   poor laboratory techniques, especially in weighing data

2.28   a.   reactant
       b.   Example:
            Since the K_{sp} is small the amount that dissolves is very small. A small K_{sp} means a small amount of product is formed or the reactants are favored. The equilibrium is far to the left (reactant) side of the reaction.

2.29

Reaction Coordinate

2.30   A saturated solution of $PbCl_2$ is a system that is in equilibrium. The rate of dissolving is equal to the rate of recrystallization.

2.31   a.   increased
       b.   The Cl^- caused a stress that could only be overcome by reducing the (Cl^-) which resulted in the precipitation.

2.32   a.   increased
       b.   The added Pb^{+2} must cause a disequalibrium that will result in a shift toward the reactant's side and result in a precipitation of $PbCl_2$.
       c.   yes
       d.   The resulting precipitation is caused by the increased probability of Pb^{+2} and Cl^- colliding and helps to decrease the (Pb^{+2}) to offset the added Pb^{+2}.

2.33   The equilibrium is between Pb^{+2} and Cl^-. The added $NaNO_3$ does not have ions that affect the Pb^{+2} or Cl^- concentration. Therefore, no stress is put on the $PbCl_2 \rightleftharpoons Pb^{+2} + 2Cl^-$.

2.34   The common ion effect is the principle that the addition of ions common to a system affect that system. Therefore, any equilibrium system will be affected by the addition or subtraction of ions common to that equilibrium.

2.35   To get a precipitate to form, a saturated solution must be supplied with common ions.

2.36   a. $[Ba^{+2}][SO_4^{-2}]$
       b. $[Zn^{+2}][OH^-]^2$
       c. $[Ca^{+2}]^3[PO_4^{-3}]^2$

2.37   a.   yes
       b. $K_{sp} = [Pb^{+2}][SO_4^{-2}] =$
            $[0.002][0.001] = 0.000002$
            $= 2 \times 10^{-6}$
            $2 \times 10^{-6} > 1.3 \times 10^{-8}$

2.38　a.　yes
　　　b.　10 ml diluted to 1,000 =
　　　　　$\frac{1}{100}$ the concentration

　　　　　$(\frac{1}{100})(1.0 \text{ M}) = 0.01 \text{ M AgNO}_3$

　　　　　$[Ag^+] = 0.01 \text{ M } [Cl^-] =$
　　　　　$1.0 \times 10^{-5} \text{ M}$

　　　　　$[Ag^+][Cl^-] = [1 \times 10^{-2}]$
　　　　　$[1 \times 10^{-5}] = 1 \times 10^{-7}$
　　　　　$1.7 \times 10^{-10} < 1 \times 10^{-7}$

　　　　　Therefore, a precipitate
　　　　　will form.

2.39　$AgCl \rightleftharpoons Ag^+ + Cl^-$
　　　$[Ag^+] = [Cl^-]$
　　　let $x = [Ag^+] = [Cl^-]$
　　　　$x^2 = [Ag^+][Cl^-] = 2.15 \times 10^{-8}$
　　　　$x = \sqrt{2.15 \times 10^{-8}}$
　　　　　$= 1.47 \times 10^{-4}$
　　　∴ 1.47×10^{-4} moles AgCl
　　　　dissolve/L

2.40　$0.0059\text{g} = 0.0000399$ moles
　　　$SrCO_3 \rightleftharpoons Sr^{+2} + CO_3^{-2}$
　　　　1　:　1　:　1
　　　$[Sr^{+2}] = [CO_3^{-2}] = 0.0000399$
　　　　$K_{sp} = [0.0000399]^2 =$
　　　　　　$[3.99 \times 10^{-5}]^2 =$
　　　　　　　1.59×10^{-9}

2.41　$K_{sp} = [Ag^+][Cl^-] = 1.7 \times 10^{-10}$
　　　$[Ag^+] = [Cl^-]$
　　　$[Ag^+] = \sqrt{1.7 \times 10^{-10}}$
　　　　　$= 1.3 \times 10^{-5}$
　　　$K_{sp} = [Ag^+]^2[CrO_4^{-2}] = 9 \times 10^{-12}$
　　　$[Ag^+] + [Ag^+] = [CrO_4^{-2}]$
　　　let $x = [CrO_4^{-2}]$; $2x = [Ag^+]$
　　　$[2x][2x][x] = 9 \times 10^{-12}$
　　　　　$4x^3 = 9 \times 10^{-12}$
　　　　　　$x = 1.2 \times 10^{-4}$
　　　　$[Ag^+] = 2.4 \times 10^{-4}$
　　　∴ The concentration of Ag^+ in
　　　AgCl is much less than in
　　　Ag_2CrO_4.

2.42　a.　increase
　　　b.　more
　　　c.　The crystal is less stable
　　　　　due to the increased inter-
　　　　　vibration of the ions. Since
　　　　　the ions are vibrating more
　　　　　than at the low temperature,
　　　　　the crystal is less stable
　　　　　and dissolves more easily.

2.43　a.　sol
　　　b.　sol
　　　c.　sol
　　　d.　low
　　　e.　low
　　　f.　sol
　　　g.　sol
　　　h.　sol
　　　i.　low
　　　j.　low
　　　k.　sol
　　　l.　low
　　　m.　sol
　　　n.　sol
　　　o.　sol

2.44　a.　AgBr--the other bromides
　　　　　are soluble in water
　　　b.　Cu_2S and FeS--the sulfide
　　　　　calcium is soluble in water
　　　c.　$CaCO_3$

2.45　a.　very few suds, cloudy appear-
　　　　　ance, scummy layer on top
　　　b.　much suds, clear solution
　　　c.　much suds, clear solution

2.46　Example:
　　　There are ions (substances) in
　　　the tap water that react with the
　　　soap to form insoluble products.

2.47　a.　There is a cloudy film on the
　　　　　glass.
　　　b.　There is no evidence of a
　　　　　residue.
　　　c.　A slight film remains--looks a
　　　　　little like salt crystals.

2.48 Suds or Scum
scum
scum
suds
suds
scum
suds
suds
suds
suds

2.49 a. $Ca^{+2}Cl^-$
b. $Fe^{+3}Cl^-$
c. $Mg^{+2}OH^-$

2.50 The Ca, Fe, and Mg are the only ones that always give a scum. The Cl^- and OH^- do not always give a scum and are therefore not the ions that produce the scum.

2.51 A soap solution added to $CaCl_2$ will form a scum; the soap added to NaCl will form suds

2.52 Example:
Several tests might work. One might be this: Put several drops of each on separate glass plates and evaporate the water.

III. SECTION THREE

3.1 a.

Reaction Coordinate

b.

Reaction Coordinate

3.2 a. products
b. reactants

3.3 The second H^+ is more tightly held to the HS^- than the H^+ is held to the H_2S because the negative S^{-2} has a stronger attraction for the H^+ than the HS^- has for the H^+. Two negatives are stronger than one.

3.4 true

3.5 false

3.6 true

3.7 false

3.8 false

3.9 true

3.10 true

3.11 Reaction
vigorous bubbling and foaming
good bubbling rate - no foam
a few bubbles
no visible reaction

How Fast?
rapid
moderate
slow
none

3.12 a. CO_2 (carbon dioxide)
b. CO_2
c. The effervescence is a test for limestone. A drop or two on the test rock would show whether or not limestone is present.
d. $CaCO_3 + 2HCl \rightleftharpoons CaCl_2 + H_2O + CO_2$

3.13 **adult check**

3.14 NH_2^-

3.15 I^-

3.16 Any order:
a. bitter, flat, or brackish taste (or feels soapy)
b. turns blue litmus red
c. accepts H^+

3.17 OH^- (hydroxide)

3.18   These values are reciprical values of each other. A large K_a means a small K_b.

3.19
a. 0
b. 7
c. 7
d. The two numbers are the same absolute value.
e. yes
f. The sum of pH and pOH is equal to 14.

3.20

$[H_3O^+]$	$[OH^-]$	pH	pOH
10^1	10^{-15}	-1	15
10^0	10^{-14}	0	14
10^{-1}	10^{-13}	1	13
10^{-2}	10^{-12}	2	12
10^{-3}	10^{-11}	3	11
10^{-4}	10^{-10}	4	10
10^{-5}	10^{-9}	5	9
10^{-6}	10^{-8}	6	8
10^{-7}	10^{-7}	7	7
10^{-8}	10^{-6}	8	6
10^{-9}	10^{-5}	9	5
10^{-10}	10^{-4}	10	4
10^{-11}	10^{-3}	11	3
10^{-12}	10^{-2}	12	2
10^{-13}	10^{-1}	13	1
10^{-14}	10^0	14	0
10^{-15}	10^1	15	-1

3.21
a. $pH = \log\dfrac{1}{[H^+]} = \log\dfrac{1}{3 \times 10^{-5}}$

$\log = \dfrac{10^5}{3} = \log 10^5 - \log 3$

$= 5 - 0.48 = 4.52$

b. 9.48

c. $[H^+][OH^-] = 1 \times 10^{-14}$

$[H^+] = \dfrac{1 \times 10^{-14}}{3 \times 10^{-10}}$

$= 0.33 \times 10^{-4}$

$= 3.3 \times 10^{-5}$

$pH = \log\dfrac{1}{[3.3 \times 10^{-5}]}$

$= \log 10^{-5} - \log 3.3$

$= 5.0 - 0.52 = 4.48$

d. $3.6 = 4 - 0.4$

$= \log 10^4 - \log 2.5$

$= \log\dfrac{1}{2.5 \times 10^{-4}}$

$= \log\dfrac{1}{[H^+]}$

$[H^+] = 2.5 \times 10^{-4}$

3.22
a. acid
   acid
   base
   base
   acid
   acid
   base
b. The H^+ was different in each solution.
c. A pH will always be assigned because H^+ will always be present in a $HB \rightleftharpoons H^+ + B^-$.
d. The HCl is a stronger acid (ioninzes to a greater extent than does the $HC_2H_3O_2$), or the $C_2H_3O_2^-$ is a stronger base than the Cl^-.
e. yes
f. The $NaHCO_3$ has a lower pH value than the Na_2CO_3 because the CO_3^{-2} ion is a stronger base than the HCO_3^- ion.

3.23   Examples:
a. the doctor in blood analysis
b. the farmer in growing crops
c. the chemist in separation of **chemicals**

3.24
a. decrease
b. The $[H^+][OH^-] = 10^{-14}$ for all combinations of H^+ and OH^-. Therefore, if the $[H^+]$ increases, the $[CH^-]$ must decrease.
c. 10^{-10}

3.25
a. $NaOH \rightleftharpoons Na^+ + OH^-$; 0.010 mole of NaOH yields 0.010 mole OH^-
The $[OH^-] = 0.010$ M, or 10^{-2}
b. $[H^+][OH^-] = 10^{-14}$
$[H^+][10^{-2}] = 10^{-14}$
$[H^+] = 10^{-12}$

3.26
a. shift to the right
b. Because the OH^- ion is a stronger base than the CH_3COO^- ion, the added OH^- will force the equilibrium to the right.
c. one
d. The CH_3COOH has only one potential acid hydrogen. Therefore, the neutralization ratio is 1:1 and one mole of OH^- will be needed.

3.27 $11.7 M = 1.17 \times 10^1 M$
$[H^+] = 1.17 \times 10^1 \underline{N} 1 \times 10^1$
$[H^+][OH^-] = 10^{-14}$
$[1 \times 10^1][OH^-] = 10^{-14}$
$[OH^-] = 10^{-15}$

3.28   a. $0.009 g = 1.53 \times 10^{-4}$ moles
$K_{sp} = [Mg^{+2}][OH^-]^2$
$\quad\quad = [1.53 \times 10^{-4}][2(1.53 \times 10^{-4})]^2$
$\quad\quad = [1.53 \times 10^{-4}][3.06 \times 10^{-4}]^2$
$\quad\quad = 1.43 \times 10^{-11}$
     b.   Because the K_{sp} is small, few ions are available to conduct a current.
     c. $[OH^-] = 3.06 \times 10^{-4}$

3.29   a.   1
     b.   2
     c.   3
     d.   1
     e.   0.1
     f.   0.1
     g.   1
     h.   1
     i.   2
     j.   1
     k.   .5
     l.   .9
     m.   .333

3.30   a. $(43.2)(0.15) = (20.5)(x)$
$\quad\quad\quad\quad\quad\quad x = 0.32$
     b. $M = 0.16$

3.31   the product of an acid-base neutralization reaction

3.32   Acid + Base $\rightleftharpoons$ Salt + water

3.33   c

3.34   a

3.35   a

3.36   b

3.37   c

3.38   a

3.39   b

3.40   c

IV.   SECTION FOUR

4.1   a.   zinc
     b.   zinc
     c.   copper
     d.   zinc

4.2   a.   Zn
     b.   Pb
     c.   Cu

4.3   a.   +0.76
     b.   -0.34
     c.   +0.13
     d.   +1.66

4.4   a.   +1.66 = Al
     b.   +0.76 = Zn
     c.   +0.13 = Pb
     d.   -0.34 = Cu
     e.   yes

4.5   51,654.4 cal

4.6 $\log K_{eq} = 37.966$
$K_{eq} = 9.25 \times 10^{37}$

4.7   a.   Al-Pb
$$2(Al^0 \rightleftharpoons Al^{+3} + 3e^-)$$
$$3(Pb^{+2} + 2e^- \rightleftharpoons Pb^0)$$
$$\overline{2Al + 3Pb^{+2} \rightleftharpoons 2Al^{+3} + 3Pb}$$
$$\begin{array}{r} 1.66 \\ -0.13 \\ \hline +1.53 \text{ volts} \end{array}$$

     b.   Al-Zn
$$2(Al \rightleftharpoons Al^{+3} + 3e^-)$$
$$3(Zn^{+2} + 2e^- \rightleftharpoons Zn^0)$$
$$\overline{2Al + 3Zn^{+2} \rightleftharpoons 2Al^{+3} + 3Zn}$$
$$\begin{array}{r} 1.66 \\ -0.76 \\ \hline +0.90 \text{ volts} \end{array}$$

     c.   Al-Cu
$$2(Al^0 \rightleftharpoons Al^{+3} + 3e^-)$$
$$3(2e^- + Cu^{+2} \rightleftharpoons Cu^0)$$
$$\overline{2Al^0 + 3Cu^{+2} \rightleftharpoons 2Al^{+3} + 3Cu^0}$$
$$\begin{array}{r} 1.66 \\ +.34 \\ \hline 2.00 \text{ volts} \end{array}$$

d. Pb-Zn

$$Zn^0 \rightleftharpoons Zn^{+2} + 2e^-$$
$$\underline{2e^- + Pb^{+2} \rightleftharpoons Pb^0}$$
$$Zn + Pb^{+2} \rightleftharpoons Pb^0 + Zn^{+2}$$

$$\begin{array}{r} 0.76 \\ \underline{-0.13} \\ 0.63 \text{ volts} \end{array}$$

e. Pb-Cu

$$Pb \rightleftharpoons Pb^{+2} + 2e^-$$
$$\underline{Cu^{+2} + 2e^- \rightleftharpoons Cu}$$
$$Pb^0 + Cu^{+2} \rightleftharpoons Pb^{+2} + Cu$$

$$\begin{array}{r} 0.13 \\ \underline{+0.34} \\ 0.47 \text{ volts} \end{array}$$

f. Zn-Cu

$$Zn^0 \rightleftharpoons Zn^{+2} + 2e^-$$
$$\underline{Cu^{+2} + 2e^- \rightleftharpoons Cu}$$
$$Zn + Cu^{+2} \rightleftharpoons Zn^{+2} + Cu$$

$$\begin{array}{r} 0.76 \\ \underline{+0.34} \\ 1.10 \text{ volts} \end{array}$$

4.8 meter error, variables in concentration, variable temperatures

4.9 a. $2(e^- + Fe^{+3} \rightleftharpoons Fe^{+2})$
$$2Cl^- \rightleftharpoons Cl_2 + 2e^-$$

$$\begin{array}{r} 0.77 \\ \underline{-1.36} \\ -0.59 \text{ (not possible)} \end{array}$$

b.
$$Mg \rightleftharpoons 2e^- + Mg^{+2}$$
$$\underline{2e^- + Br_2 \rightleftharpoons 2Br^-}$$
$$Mg + Br_2 \rightleftharpoons MgBr_2$$

$$\begin{array}{r} 2.37 \\ \underline{1.06} \\ +3.43 \text{ (possible)} \end{array}$$

c.
$$Cu \rightleftharpoons Cu^{+2} + 2e^-$$
$$\underline{2e^- + 2H^+ \rightleftharpoons H_2}$$

$$\begin{array}{r} -0.34 \\ \underline{0.00} \\ -0.34 \text{ (not possible)} \end{array}$$

d.
$$(Zn \rightleftharpoons Zn^{+2} + 2e^-)$$
$$\underline{2e^- + F_2 \rightleftharpoons 2F^-}$$
$$F_2 + Zn \rightleftharpoons ZnF_2$$

$$\begin{array}{r} 0.76 \\ \underline{+2.87} \\ 3.63 \text{ (possible)} \end{array}$$

4.9 e.
$$Mg^{+2} + 2e^- \rightleftharpoons Mg$$
$$\underline{2Ag \rightleftharpoons 2Ag^+ + 2e^-}$$

$$\begin{array}{r} -2.37 \\ \underline{-0.80} \\ -3.17 \text{ (not possible)} \end{array}$$

4.10 a. $O = -2$
 $N = +1$
b. $H = +1$
 $S = +6$
 $O = -2$
c. $K = +1$
 $Cl = -1$
d. $C = +2$
 $O = -2$
e. $N = +2$
 $O = -2$
f. $Mn = +4$
 $O = -2$
g. $N = +5$
 $O = -2$
h. $K = +1$
 $Mn = +7$
 $O = -2$
i. $C = +4$
 $O = -2$
j. $N = +4$
 $O = -2$
k. 0

4.11 a. oxidizing agent = Mn^{+7}
reducing agent = S^{-2}

$K = +1$	$Cl = -1$
$Mn = +7$	$Mn = +2$
$H = +1$	$Cl = -1$
$S = -2$	$H = +1$
$H = +1$	$O = -2$
$Cl = -1$	$S = 0$
$K = +1$	$O = -2$

$$2(5e^- + Mn^{+7} \longrightarrow Mn^{+2})$$
$$5(S^{-2} \longrightarrow S^0 + 2e^-)$$
$$2KMnO_4 + 5H_2S + 6HCl \rightleftharpoons 2KCl$$
$$+ 2MnCl_2 + 8H_2O + 5S$$

b. oxidizing agents = S^{+6}
reducing agent = Br^-
$$2Br^- \longrightarrow Br_2 , \quad S^{+6} \longrightarrow S^{+4}$$
$$2(-1 \longrightarrow 0 + e^-), \quad 2e^- + 6 \longrightarrow + 4$$
$$2HBr + H_2SO_4 \rightleftharpoons SO_2 + Br_2 + 2H_2O$$

c. oxidizing agent = N^{+5}
reducing agent = Cu^0
$Cu^0 \longrightarrow Cu^{+2} + 2e^-$
$3(0 \longrightarrow +2 + 2e)$
$3e^- + N^{+5} \longrightarrow N^{+2}$
$2(+3e^- + 5 \longrightarrow +2)$
$3Cu + 8HNO_3 \longrightarrow 3Cu(NO_3)_2 + 4H_2O + 2NO$

d. oxidizing agent = Al^{+3}
reducing agent = Na^0
$3e^- + Al^{+3} \longrightarrow Al^0$
$Na^0 \longrightarrow Na^{+1} + e$
$3(0 \longrightarrow +1 + e)$
$3e^- + 3 \longrightarrow 0$
$AlCl_3 + 3Na \rightleftharpoons 3NaCl + Al$

4.12 E^o for Co = .28, E^o for H_2 = .00, yes, will dissolve

4.13 $10FeSO_4 + 2KMnO_4 + 8H_2SO_4 \rightleftharpoons$
$2MnSO_4 + 8H_2O + 5Fe_2(SO_4)_3 + K_2SO_4$

4.14 $2Pb_3H_4IO_6 + 14HCl + H_3AsO_3 \rightleftharpoons$
$6PbCl_2 + 2ICl + H_3AsO_4 + 11H_2O$

4.15 The sulfur caused a black spot on the silver.

4.16 $2Ag + S \rightleftharpoons Ag_2S$

4.17
$Al^0 \rightleftharpoons Al^{+3} + 3e^-$
$3(Ag^+ + e^- \rightleftharpoons Ag)$
$\overline{3Ag^+ + Al \rightleftharpoons 3Ag + Al^{+3}}$

1.66 volts
0.80 volts
+2.46 volts

4.18 Observations
apple turns very brown and soft
less brown than #1
some brown
little brown color appears
looks like the original slice
a little brown - not as fresh as #5
about like #6

4.19 yes

4.20 Yes. However, the other preservatives are more dangerous to the health and should be limited in their usage.

4.21 A little. Natural Vitamin C is a better reducing agent.

4.22 Aluminum is a strong reducing agent and the acid would act as an oxidizing agent.

4.23 Aluminum is a strong reducing agent and silver is an oxidizing agent.

4.24 $CuSO_4$ would form from the Cu wires and the H_2SO_4 in the battery.

4.25 K_{eq} would be 1×10^{-7}; no reaction is taking place that releases electrons.

4.26
a. +4
b. +2
c. +4
d. +6
e. +5
f. +4
g. +5

4.27
a. oxidation
b. $M^{+2} \rightleftharpoons M^{+6} + 4e^-$

4.28
$Cu^0 \rightleftharpoons Cu^{+2} + 2e^-$
$3e^- + Cr^{+3} \rightleftharpoons Cr^0$

-0.34
-0.74
-1.08 volts

Nothing will happen because the voltage is negative.

4.29
a. Na^+, O^{-2}, H^+, SO_4^{-2}
b. 8
c. 5
d. $5S^{-2} + 2Mn^{+7} \rightleftharpoons 5S^0 + 2Mn^{+2}$

4.30 d

4.31 d

121

1.1   a.   C; H_2O
       b.   yes
       c.   Since 11 H_2SO_4 molecules are
          on both the products and
          reactants sides, none are used
          or changed in the reaction.
       d. H_2O
       e.   yes
       f.   exothermic
       g.   reactants
       h.

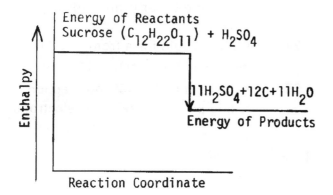

1.2   Urea is an organic compound produced by animal metabolism.

1.3   This theory proposed that all organic compounds contained a "vital spirit" since they all were the result of living **organisms**. No organic compound could be produced in the laboratory because no one had a bottle of "vital spirit" to make organic compounds.

1.4   Wohler's contribution was that he accidentally produced crystals of urea from an inorganic compound called ammonium cyanate.

1.5

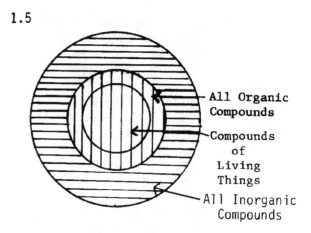

1.6   true

1.7   false

1.8   1 million

1.9   100,000

1.10   thousands

1.11   coal

1.12   Either order:
       a.   hydrogen
       b.   carbon

1.13   sulfur compound

1.14   Any order:
       a.   methane
       b.   ethane
       c.   propane

1.15   Any order:
       a.   pentane
       b.   hexane
       c.   heptane
       d.   octane
       e.   nonane
       f.   decane

1.16   coke

1.17 Any order:
   a. buildings
   b. paper
   c. heat (energy)

1.18 pollution

1.19 a. 40
   b. 206

1.20 false

1.21 true

1.22 true

1.23 true

1.24 2; 3; 4; 3

1.25 a. CH_4
   b. C_2H_6
   c. C_6H_{14}
   d. $C_{10}H_{22}$
   e. $C_{13}H_{28}$

1.26 increases

II. SECTION TWO

2.1 a. 6
   b. 6
   c.

2.2 $1s^2\ 2s^2\ 2p^2$

2.3 a. B
   b. 2
   c. 1
   d. 3
   e. inert gas
   f. Electrons naturally repel each
      other. Therefore, electrons in
      the same sublevel will remain
      unpaired in separate orbitals
      until each orbital in that
      sublevel has at least one
      electron. (Review Science
      LIFEPAC 1104, page 36.)
   g. 4

2.4 Volcanoes have both high pressure
   and high temperature which are
   necessary to produce diamonds.

2.5 Example:
   Silicon carbide should be a hard,
   three-dimensional compound because
   both elements occur in the same
   column as carbon.

2.6 Example:
   Both can share electrons like
   carbon can with itself because they
   have the same electron properties
   since they both occur in the same
   column and have the same valence
   electron structure.

2.7 a. SiO_2
   Example:
   b. The melting point and boiling
      point of quartz are very high,
      and therefore, its properties
      are much like diamond which is
      a network solid. The low
      melting point of CO_2 indicates
      weak bonds holding it in the
      solid state.

2.8 a. diamond
   b. graphite
   c. diamond

2.9 a

2.10 b

2.11 b

2.12 c

2.13 a

2.14 b

2.15 a

2.16 c

2.17 Column VII

2.18 Column I

2.19 CsF

2.20 a. 0
      b. 100
      c. 0
      d. 100
      e. 4
      f. 96

2.21 true

2.22 true

2.23 false

2.24 true

2.25 false

2.26 b

2.27 e

2.28 a

2.29 d

2.30 f

III. SECTION THREE

3.1 combustion

3.2 C_nH_{2n+2}

3.3 structural

3.4 attraction

3.5 a. how many carbons
     b. alkane

3.6 2; 13; 8; 10

3.7 $2 C_8H_{18} + 25 O_2 \rightleftharpoons 16 CO_2 + 18 H_2O$

3.8 $C_3H_8 + 5 O_2 \rightleftharpoons 3 CO_2 + 4 H_2O$

3.9

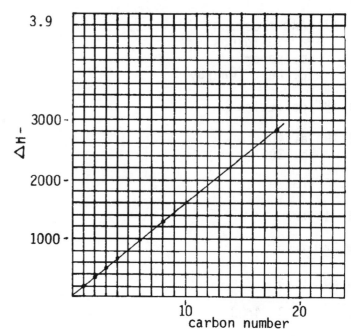

3.10

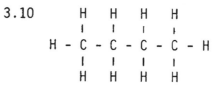

n- butane

isobutane

3.11 OPTIONAL:

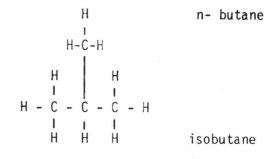

124

3.11 cont.

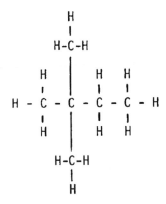

3.12 false

3.13 true

3.14 true

3.15 false

3.16 true

3.17 b

3.18 h

3.19 a

3/20 f

3.21 j

3.22 i

3.23 g

3.24 c

3.25 d

3.26 1; 3; 2; 2

3.27 2; 5; 4; 2

3.28 1; 2; 1

3.29 false

3.30 false

3.31 a. C_nH_{2n+2}
b. combustion (substitution)
c. C_2H_6

3.32 a. C_nH_{2n}
b. addition
c. C_2H_4

3.33 a. C_nH_{2n-2}
b. addition
c. C_2H_2

3.34 a. C_3H_8
b. C_6H_{14}
c. C_9H_{20}
d. $C_{12}H_{26}$

3.35 a. C_3H_6
b. C_6H_{12}
c. C_9H_{18}
d. $C_{12}H_{24}$

3.36 a. C_3H_4
b. C_6H_{10}
c. C_9H_{16}
d. $C_{12}H_{22}$

3.37 a. not possible, only one carbon
b. not possible, only one carbon

3.38 a. ethene
b. ethyne

3.39 a. propene
b. propyne

3.40 a. butene
b. butyne

3.41 a. pentene
b. pentyne

3.42 a. hexene
      b. hexyne

3.43 a. heptene
      b. heptyne

3.44 a. octene
      b. octyne

3.45 a. nonene
      b. nonyne

3.46 a. decene
      b. decyne

1.1

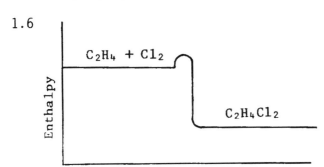

1.2   substitution

1.3   Examples; any order:
a.   chloroform
b.   Freon
c.   phosgene

1.4 $CH_4 + 4F_2 \rightarrow CF_4 + 4HF$

1.5   1, 2, 1, 2

1.6

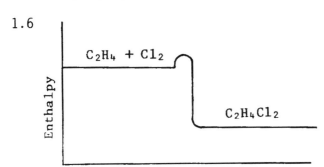

1.7   Example:
DDT is absorbed by birds (eagles) and interferes with the calcium utilization in egg-shell production. This blockage causes the birds to lay soft-shelled eggs. These soft eggs are easily broken and destroyed, causing a decline in the species population.

1.8   addition

1.9   1, 1, 1

1.10 The reaction between alkanes and halogens is substitution, occurs slowly, and requires energy. The reaction between alkenes and halogens is by addition, occurs almost spontaneously, and needs little activation energy.

1.11 a. F_2
b.   Flourine has a higher electronegativity; therefore, is more reactive.

2.1   Either order:
a.   oxygen
b.   hydrogen

2.2   Examples; any order:
a.   methyl alcohol
b.   isopropyl alcohol
c.   ethylene glycol

2.3   Alcohol with more than one -OH group on each molecule is a polyhydroxy alcohol.

2.4   a.   1, 2, 1
b.   2, 3, 2, 4

2.5   Fermentation is a chemical process in which complex organic molecules are broken down into simpler compounds, one of which is ethanol.

2.6   any alkyl (H-C) group

2.7   a. CH_3OH
b. C_4H_9OH
c. $C_8H_{17}OH$

2.8   The longer the R-group, the less reactive is the molecule.

2.9   Primary alcohols have the -OH group on a terminal (end) carbon while the secondary alcohols have the -OH group on carbons that are nonterminal.

2.10 aldehyde

2.11 **carboxylic acid**

2.12 Examples; any order:
a.   formic
b.   acetic
c.   palmitic

2.13 e

2.14 c

2.15　a

2.16　d

2.17　b

2.18　1, 1, 1, 1

2.19　1, 23, 16, 16

2.20

　　a.　$H_3C-C\overset{OH}{\underset{H}{\big\langle}}_H + H-C\overset{O}{\underset{OH}{\big\langle}} \rightarrow$

　　　　$H_3C-C\overset{H}{\underset{H}{\big\langle}}\,\overset{O}{\underset{O}{\big\|}}C-H + H_2O$

　　b.　$H_3C-CH_2-C\overset{H\ \ OH}{\underset{H}{\big\langle}} + H_3C-CH_2-C\overset{O}{\underset{OH}{\big\langle}} \rightarrow$

　　　　$H_3C-CH_2-C\overset{H}{\underset{O}{\big\langle}}-H\ \overset{O}{\underset{}{\big\|}}C-CH_2-CH_3 + H_2O$

　　c.　$H_3COH + H-C\overset{O}{\underset{OH}{\big\langle}} \rightarrow H_3C-O-\overset{O}{\overset{\|}{C}}-H + H_2O$

2.21　Examples; any order:
　　　a.　ethyl formate
　　　b.　propyl propionate
　　　c.　methyl formate

2.22　$Keg = \dfrac{[C_3H_6O_2][H_2O]}{[C_2H_4O_2][CH_4O]}$

2.23　c

2.24　e

2.25　a

2.26　f

2.27　b

2.28　true

2.29　true

2.30　false

2.31　false

2.32　true

III. SECTION THREE

3.1　ammonia

3.2　any hydrocarbon group whether saturated or unsaturated

3.3　ethyl

3.4　R-

3.5　two

3.6　d

3.7　a

3.8　c

3.9　b

3.10　e

3.11　g

3.12　$R-X + 2\ NH_3 \rightarrow R-NH_2 + NH_4X$

3.13　Amines are named by naming the R- group(s) and adding the word amine.

3.14　Either order:
　　　a.　amines
　　　b.　acids

3.15　$-\overset{O}{\overset{\|}{C}}-\underset{H}{\overset{}{N}}-$

3.16　Either order:
　　　a.　reacting ammonia with esters
　　　b.　reacting amines with esters

3.17　ammonia

3.18　$H_2N-CH-C\overset{O}{\underset{OH}{\big\langle}}$
　　　$\quad\quad\ \ \underset{R}{|}$

3.19   Either order:
        a. amine (-NH$_2$)
        b. acid (-COOH)

3.20   peptide (amide)

3.21 $$\begin{matrix} O & H \\ \| & | \\ -C & -N- \end{matrix}$$

3.22   Hint: Answers should include
                these points.
        1. probability evidence of random
           synthesis and
        2. the evidence of left-handed
           proteins (amino acids).

3.23   Basically this passage means that
        even though all evidence points
        to a divine Creator, man will
        be so satisfied in his own
        "wisdom" that he will deny God's
        existence.

3.24   **adult check**

3.25   Either order:
        a. protein
        b. nonprotein

3.26   protein

3.27   substrate

3.28   metallic

3.29   The enzyme aligns itself with the
        reactants. If the bonds of the
        enzyme and substrate do not align
        properly nothing happens.

3.30   A "false substrate" is a chemical
        that has similar properties to
        the true substrate. However, the
        "false substrate" is able to
        attract an enzyme or one of the
        reactants and tie it up so it
        cannot react in its normal way.
        The "false substrate" fools the
        reactants and therefore inhibits
        the normal reaction.

1.1   a.   0.1; 10,000; 100,000
       b.   0.0012; 1.20; 1,200
       c.   0.000001; 0.001; 1.0
       d.   0.063; 6,300; 63,000
       e.   0.0001263; 0.1263; 12.63
       f.   0.0315; 3,150; 31,500
       g.   536; 53,600; 536,000
       h.   0.0000192; 0.0192; 19.2
       i.   0.00684; 684; 6,840
       j.   0.00000930; 0.00930; 0.930
       k.   61,390; 6,139,000; 61,390,000
       l.   0.0001516; 15.16; 151.6
       m. 0.000000031; 0.000031; 0.031
       n.   0.1234; 123.4; 12,340
       o.   0.00036; 0.036; 0.36
       p.   0.00366; 3.66; 366

1.2   a.   2,100; 2,100
       b.   1.05; 1.05
       c.   941; .941
       d.   100.5; 100.5
       e.   10,300; 10.300
       f.   0.025; 0.000025
       g.   22,400; 22,400
       h.   12.86; 0.01286
       i.   321.; 321.
       j.   22.4; 0.0224
       k.   25.; 25.

1.3   a.   0.1; 10,000; 100,000
       b.   0.00000134; 0.00134; 0.134
       c.   0.00001011; 1.011; 10.11
       d.   6.84; 684; 6,840
       e.   0.000854; 0.8540; 854.0
       f.   0.0000379; 3.79; 37.9
       g.   0.01084; 10.84; 1,084
       h.   0.00905; 9.05; 9,050
       i.   0.00165; 0.165; 1.65

1.4   e

1.5   a

1.6   b

1.7   d

1.8   g

1.9   c

1.10   a.   3
       b.   3
       c.   3
       d.   5
       e.   3
       f.   4
       g.   4
       h.   2
       i.   4
       j.   6

1.11   a.   23.46
       b.   0.0064
       c.   0.095
       d.   6.36

1.12   a. 3.24×10^4
       b. 5.43×10^{-4}
       c. 1.3×10^{-13}
       d. 1.8×10^1

1.13   a.   0.00897
       b.   3
       c.   34,000
       d.   602,000,000,000,000,000,000,000

1.14   a. 9.6×10^{14}
       b. 1.2×10^{28}
       c. 2×10^8
       d. 2×10^8

1.15   a. Ag_2O
       b. KCl
       c. AlF_3
       d. SnO_2
       e. $CaBr_2$
       f. CsI
       g. $SiBr_4$

1.16   a.   57
       b.   45

1.17   Metals are in the lower left and the nonmetals are in the upper right.

1.18   a.   E
       b.   C
       c.   E
       d.   C
       e.   C
       f.   E
       g.   C
       h.   E
       i.   C

1.19   a.   phase (physical)
      b.   chemical
      c.   chemical
      d.   chemical
      e.   chemical
      f.   physical

1.20   f

1.21   e

1.22   b

1.23   g

1.24   a

1.25   d

1.26   Either order:
      a.   pure substance
      b.   mixture

1.27   Either order:
      a.   metals
      b.   nonmetals

1.28   Either order:
      a.   homogeneous
      b.   heterogeneous

1.29   a.   Tyndall
      b.   Brownian

1.30   nitrogen

1.31   Example:
Gaseous mixtures are in continuous random motion (Kinetic Molecular Theory) and because the motion is random, the gases stay evenly mixed instead of layering or settling out of the atmosphere.

1.32   a.   M
      b.   M
      c.   M
      d.   P
      e.   M
      f.   M

1.33   a.   larger
      b.   smaller
      c.   guess about 6.5
      d. $(9.0)(500) = (750)(V_2)$
         $V_2 = 6.0$ ml

1.34   a.   291
      b.   210
      c.   556

1.35   a.   740 mm Hg
      b.   10.0 L
      c.   300
      d.   370 mm Hg
      e.   200
      f.

$$\frac{(740)(10.0)}{300} = \frac{(370)(V_2)}{200}$$

$$V_2 = \frac{(200)(740)(10.0)}{(300)(370)} = \frac{(2)(2)10}{(3)(1)} = \frac{40}{3} = 13.3 \text{ L}$$

1.36   a.   Boyle's Law
      b. $(1 \text{ atm})(0.75 \text{ L}) = (P_2)(0.15 \text{ L})$
         $P_2 = 5$ atm

1.37   a.   Charles' Law
      b. $\dfrac{1 \text{ L}}{90° \text{ K}} = \dfrac{V_2}{270° \text{ K}}$

         $V_2 = 3$ L

1.38 a. 30.
      b. 46.
      c. 58.
      d. 136.
      e. 352
      f. 148
      g. 63
      h. 330
      i. 17.
      j. 232.
      k. 62
      l. 44.

1.39 a. H; 1; Cl; 1; __; __; 36
      b. Na; 2; C; 1; O; 3; 106
      c. Ba; 1; N; 2; O; 6; 261
      d. C; 6; H; 12; O; 6; 180
      e. Fe; 2; O; 3; __; __; 160
      f. H; 2; S; 1; O; 4; 98
      g. Ag; 1; N; 1; O; 3; 170
      h. H; 2; O; 1; __; __; 18

1.40 a. 32.0 g
      b. 2.0 g
      c. 17.2 g
      d. 28.0 g
      e. 44.0 g

1.41 yes

1.42 Since all five gases are under the same conditions, they have the same number of molecules.

1.43 a. 2; 2
      b. 4; 2; 2
      c. 2; 2; 2
      d. 4; 3; 2

1.44 $\dfrac{\text{moles } CO_2}{\text{moles } O_2} = \dfrac{6}{11} = \dfrac{0.34}{x}$

$(6)(x) = (11)(0.34)$

$x = \dfrac{(11)(0.34)}{6}$ moles

$x = 0.625$ moles of O_2 needed

1.45 $\dfrac{\text{moles } H_2O}{\text{moles } CO_2} = \dfrac{10}{6} = \dfrac{x}{0.34}$

$(6)(x) = (10)(0.34)$ moles

$x = \dfrac{(10)(0.34)}{6}$ moles

$x = 0.567$ moles H_2O produced

1.46 $\dfrac{\text{moles } C_3H_{10}}{\text{moles } CO_2} = \dfrac{2}{6} = \dfrac{x}{0.34 \text{ moles}}$

$(6)(x) = (2)(0.34)$ moles

$x = \dfrac{(2)(0.34)}{6}$ moles

$x = 0.114$ moles

$(0.114 \text{ moles})\left(\dfrac{46 \text{ g}}{\text{mole}}\right) =$

5.21 g propane needed

1.47
| 1. g C_3H_{10} | → | 2. moles C_3H_{10} | → | 3. moles CO_2 | → |

| 4. liters CO_2 |

$1 \rightarrow 2$ $2 \rightarrow 3$

$\dfrac{105 \text{ g}}{46 \text{ g/moles}} = \dfrac{C_3H_{10}}{CO_2} = \dfrac{2}{6} =$

$\dfrac{2.8}{x}$

$3 \rightarrow 4$

$(6.84 \text{ moles})\left(\dfrac{22.4 \text{ L}}{\text{mole}}\right) = 153 \text{ L}$

2.28 moles C_3H_{10}

$2x = (6)(2.28)$
$x = 6.83$ moles CO_2

1.48 a. negative
      b. Thomson
      c. 1895
      d. very small
      e. outside nucleus
      f. positive
      g. Rutherford
      h. after 1909
      i. same
      j. nucleus
      k. neutral
      l. Chadwick
      m. 1931
      n. same
      o. nucleus

1.49 a. m
      b. p
      c. q
      d. o
      e. t
      f. o
      g. q
      h. s
      i. n
      j. o
      k. r

1.50 b

1.51 c

1.52 a

1.53 d

1.54 b

1.55 e

1.56 b

1.57 b

1.58 c

1.59 d

1.60 a. hydrogen; H; 1
      b. helium; He; 2
      c. lithium; Li; 2; 1
      d. boron; B; 2; 2; 1
      e. neon; Ne; 2; 2; 6
      f. magnesium; Mg; 2; 2; 6; 2
      g. argon; Ar; 2; 2; 6; 2; 6
      h. germanium; Ge; 2; 2; 6; 2; 6;
          2; 10; 2

1.61 boron

1.62 a. energy level
      b. orbital (sublevel)
      c. electron number
      d. boron

1.63 fluorine; F; $1s^2 2s^2 2p^5$

1.64 neon; Ne; $1s^2 2s^2 2p^6$

1.65 magnesium; Mg; $1s^2 2s^2 2p^6 3s^2$

1.66 phosphorus; P; $1s^2 2s^2 2p^6 3s^2 3p^3$

1.67 sulfur; S; $1s^2 2s^2 2p^6 3s^2 3p^4$

1.68 argon; Ar; $1s^2 2s^2 2p^6 3s^2 3p^6$

1.69 calcium; Ca; $1s^2 2s^2 2p^6 3s^2 3p^6 4s^2$

1.70 zinc; Zn; $1s^2 2s^2 2p^6 3s^2 3p^6 4s^2 3d^{10}$

1.71 selenium; Se; $1s^2 2s^2 2p^6 3s^2 3p^6 4s^2 3d^{10} 4p^4$

1.72 silver; Ag; $1s^2 2s^2 2p^6 3s^2 3p^6 4s^2 3d^{10} 4p^6 5s^2 4d^9$

1.73 barium; Ba; $1s^2 2s^2 2p^6 3s^2 3p^6 4s^2 3d^{10} 4p^6 5s^2 4d^{10} 5p^6 6s^2$

1.74 a.

1.75 a.   b.

      c.   d.

1.76 a.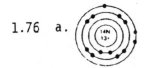

b.

1.77
a. $1s^1$; 1
b. $1s^2 2s^1$; 1
c. $1s^2 2s^2 2p^3$; 5
d. $1s^2 2s^2 2p^5$; 7
e. $1s^2 2s^2 2p^6 3s^1$; 1
f. $1s^2 2s^2 2p^6 3s^2$; 2
g. $1s^2 2s^2 2p^6 3s^2 3p^2$; 4
h. $1s^2 2s^2 2p^6 3s^2 3p^4$; 6
i. $1s^2 2s^2 2p^2$; 4
j. $1s^2 2s^2 2p^6 3s^2 3p^6$; 0

1.78
a. Cs
b. Ba
c. K
d. Li
e. K
f. Cs
g. Ba
h. Al

1.79
a. F
b. O
c. Cl
d. F
e. F
f. O
g. O
h. N

1.80
a. helium
b. lithium
c. boron
d. nitrogen
e. potassium
f. nickel

1.81
a. 11
b. 11
c. 11
d. 11
e. yes
f. Both atoms have the same atomic number.
g. Atom B has a higher energy level.
h. Atom B absorbs energy from some outside source.
i. A

j. Atom A is in its natural low energy state.

1.82
a. $^{230}_{90}$ Th
b. $^{4}_{2}$ He
c. $^{248}_{96}$ Cm
d. $^{218}_{84}$ Po
e. $^{238}_{94}$ Pu
f. $^{4}_{2}$ He; $^{0}_{-1}$ e

1.83 The Periodic Law states that the physical and chemical properties of the elements are periodic, or regularly occurring, functions of their atomic numbers. Examples of this law are atomic volume, ionization energy, atomic radii, and electronegativity.

1.84
a. +1
b. 1
c. +2
d. 2
e. +3
f. 3
g. ±4
h. 4
i. -3
j. 5
k. -2
l. 6
m. -1
n. 7
o. 0
p. 8 or 0

1.85
a. DE_2
b. DG
c. No
d. Like charges do not attract but repel, so A^{+1} and D^{+2} would not react.

1.86
a. 67
b. 22
c. 39
d. 51
e. 0
f. 4

1.87 f

1.88 c

1.89 d

1.90 f

1.91 a

1.92 a

1.93 a

1.94 a

1.95 d

1.96 e

1.97 a. ionic
b. metallic
c. covalent
d. ionic
e. covalent
f. covalent
g. covalent
h. covalent

1.98 a. H—S—H
b. bent
c. polar

1.99 a. Cl—Al(—Cl)—Cl
b. triangular
c. nonpolar

1.100 a. H-F
b. linear
c. polar

1.101 a. H—C(—H), Cl—C—Cl
b. tetrahedral
c. polar

1.102 a. Cl—Sn(—Cl), Cl—Sn—Cl
b. tetrahedral
c. nonpolar

1.103 a. F—N(—F)—F
b. F : N̈ : F, F
c. pyrimidal
d. polar

1.104 a. F-F
b. :F̈ : F̈:
c. linear
d. nonpolar

1.105 a. F—O—F
b. :Ö:, :F̈: :F̈:
c. bent
d. polar

1.106 a. Li-F
b. Li : F̈:
c. linear
d. polar

1.107 a. F-Be-F
b. :F̈ :Be: F̈:
c. linear
d. nonpolar

1.108 a. F—B(—F)—F
b. :F̈: B : F̈: :F̈:
c. triangular
d. nonpolar

1.109 a. F—C(—F), F—C—F
b. :F̈: :F̈: C :F̈: :F̈:
c. tetrahedral
d. nonpolar

1.110 a. linear
b. linear
c. triangular
d. tetrahedral
e. pyrimidal
f. bent
g. linear
h. none

II. SECTION TWO

2.1   true

2.2   false

2.3   false

2.4   true

2.5   true

2.6   false

2.7   true

2.8   false

2.9   false

2.10   true

2.11   a. 22,000 cal
       b. 331 kcal
       c. 2.4 kcal
       d. 712 kcal
       e. 94.50 kcal

2.12   O-O = +119
          C-H = + 99
          C-H = + 99
       ─────────────
       gained = +317

          C=O = -192
          O-H = -111
          O-H = -111
       ─────────────
       lost = -414

       Net = +317 + (-414) = -97 kcal

2.13   true

2.14   false

2.15   false

2.16   true

2.17   false

2.18   a

2.19   d

2.20   e

2.21   c

2.22   f

2.23   a

2.24   b

2.25   e

2.26   d

2.27   c

2.28   c

2.29   d

2.30   a

2.31   d

2.32   d

2.33   c

2.34   true

2.35   false

2.36   false

2.37   true

2.38   true

2.39   true

2.40   false

2.41   false

2.42   false

2.43   true

2.44   k

2.45   g

2.46 j

2.47 i

2.48 a

2.49 b

2.50 f

2.51 e

2.52 c

2.53 h

2.54 d

2.55 a

2.56 b

2.57 c

2.58 saturated

2.59 Any order:
    a. sour taste
    b. turn litmus red
    c. contain H
    d. react with metals

2.60 product of the reaction between acids and bases

2.61 pH

2.62 b

2.63 a

2.64 b, c, e, g

2.65 a

2.66 c

2.67 b

2.68 e

2.69 b

2.70 a. NaF
       b. $MgCl_2$
       c. AlF_3
       d. $BaCl_2$

2.71 a. $N = +1$
          $O = -2$
       b. $H = +1$
          $S = +6$
          $O = -2$
       c. $K = +1$
          $Cl = -1$
       d. $C = +2$
          $O = -2$
       e. $N = +2$
          $O = -2$
       f. $Mn = +4$
          $O = -2$
       g. $N = +5$
          $O = -2$
       h. $K = +1$
          $Mn = +7$
          $O = -2$
       i. $C = +4$
          $O = -2$
       j. $N = +4$
          $O = -2$
       k. $C = 0$

2.72 a. oxidizing agent = Mn^{+7}
          reducing agent = S^{-2}

$$2(5e^- + Mn^{+7} \rightarrow Mn^{+2})$$
$$5(S^{-2} \rightarrow S^0 + 2e^-)$$
$$\overline{10e^- + 2Mn^{+7} \rightarrow 2Mn^{+2}}$$
$$5S^{-2} \rightarrow 5S^0 + 10e^-$$
$$\overline{2Mn^{+7} + 5S^{-2} \rightarrow 2Mn^{+2} + 5S^0}$$

$$2KMnO_4 + 5H_2S + 6HCl \rightleftarrows$$
$$2KCl + 2MnCl_2 + 8H_2O + 5S$$

       b. oxidizing agent = S^{+6}
          reducing agent = $2Br^-$

$$2e^- + S^{+6} \rightarrow S^{+4}$$
$$2Br^- \rightarrow Br_2 + 2e^-$$
$$\overline{S^{+6} + 2Br^- \rightarrow S^{+4} + Br_2}$$

$$2HBr + H_2SO_4 \rightleftarrows$$
$$SO_2 + Br_2 + 2H_2O$$

3.1 I

3.2 O

3.3 I

3.4 O

3.5 O

3.6 h

3.7. c

3.8 f

3.9 i

3.10 a

3.11 e

3.12 b

3.13 d

3.14 k

3.15 g

3.16 C_nH_{2n-2}

3.17 $1s^22s^22p^2$

3.18 C_nH_{2n+2}

3.19 covalent

3.20 C_nH_{2n}

3.21 Any order:
a. coal
b. petroleum
c. plants and animals

3.22 alkene

3.23 addition

3.24 tetrahedral

3.25 alkane

3.26 j

3.27 f

3.28 e

3.29 g

3.30 a

3.31 i

3.32 k

3.33 c

3.34 b

3.35 d

3.36 substitution

3.37 addition

3.38 peptide (amide)

3.39 ammonia

3.40 true

3.41 true

3.42 false

3.43 true

3.44 true

3.45 false

SELF TEST 1

1.01   b. kilo

1.02   e. kilogram

1.03   a. milli

1.04   d. meter

1.05   c. centi

1.06   kg
       b.   0.0001056
       d.   0.00563
       e.   0.00000297
       g
       b.   0.1056
       c.   953
       e.   0.00297
       mg
       c. 953,000
       d.   5,630
       ml
       h.   32
       j.   856
       L
       g.   0.0136
       i.   0.00733
       km
       l.   0.00001
       m.   0.0000125
       o.   0.00169
       m
       m.   0.0125
       n.   180
       cm
       l.   1
       m.   1.25
       n. 18,000
       o.   169
       mm
       l.   10
       n. 180,000
       o.   1,690

1.07   kilogram; It is equal to a standard
       in France. The mass is approximately
       that of one liter of water.

1.08   one liter; 1/1000 cubic meter which
       equals 1000cm^3

1.09   meter; It equals the length of a
       standard bar in France.

SELF TEST 2

2.01   e. 1/1000

2.02   f. curved surface of a liquid

2.03   k. precision of a 50ml grad. cyl.

2.04   b. 1/100

2.05   g. unit of mass

2.06   d. unit of length

2.07   h. 1000

2.08   a. unit of volume

2.09   j. precision of a metric ruler

2.010   c. uncertainty of measurement

2.011   a. 8.80 ± 0.01 ml
        b. 5.50 ± 0.01 ml
        c. 6.82 ± 0.01 ml
        d. 2.20 ± 0.01 ml

2.012   76.0 ± 0.1mm

2.013   35.0 ± 0.1mm

2.014   104.0 ± 0.1mm

2.015   13.0 ± 0.1mm

2.016   adult check

2.017   adult check

2.018   adult check

2.019   adult check

SELF TEST 3

3.01   g. theory

3.02   h. inverse

3.03   a. qualitative

3.04   b. hypothesis

3.05   f. control

3.06   k. best fit

3.07   c. direct

3.08   j. law

3.09   e. quantitative

3.010 d. limewater

3.011 **Any order:**
       a. Unit and title for each axis
       b. Title for each graph
       c. Name of experimentor
       d. A legend when needed

3.012 a. y/x = k

3.013 c. quantitative

3.014 b. xy = k

3.015 c.

3.016 a. law

3.017 d. milli

SELF TEST 4

4.01   f. 1/1000

4.02   c. uncertainty value of measurement

4.03   g. straight line data graph

4.04   a. 1000

4.05   l. instrument to measure volume

4.06   k. numerical observation

4.07   e. instrument to measure distance

4.08   b. educated guess

4.09   h. correctness of a measurement

4.010 i. 1/100

4.011 a. cm

4.012 b. kg

4.013 c. m

4.014 a. balance

4.015 d. 1790

4.016 6.1103×10^{4}

4.017 1.325×10^{-2}

4.018 0.00385

4.019 69,830

4.020 1.86×10^{4} or 2×10^{4}

4.021 1.62×10^{-5} or 2×10^{-5}

4.022 4

4.023 5

4.024 7.32

4.025 $89.7 = 8.97 \times 10^{1}$

SELF TEST 5

5.01   j. 1/100

5.02   h. primary unit of mass

5.03   g. 10mm

5.04   i. instrument of length

5.05   c. educated guess

5.06   e. symbol for volume measurement

5.07   l. instrument of volume

5.08   b. instrument of mass

5.09   d. descriptive observation

5.010 k. symbol of temperature

5.011 cm or mm

5.012 kg

5.013 10ml

5.014 triple-beam; platform

5.015 a. The primary unit of mass is the
           kilogram, a standard mass kept
           in France.
       b. The primary unit of volume is
           the liter, which is $1000cm^3$
       c. The primary unit of distance is
           the meter, which we use as a
           standard in France.

5.016 1.6456×10^3

5.017 5.00×10^{-5}

5.018 a. 9.2 $\pm$ 0.01 ml
       b. 3.2 $\pm$ 0.01 ml
       c. 74.0 $\pm$ 0.1 ml
       d. 33.8 $\pm$ 0.1 ml

5.019 Example:

	x	y	k
a.	.1	2	20
b.	.2	4	20
c.	.3	6	20
d.	.4	8	20
e.	.5	10	20

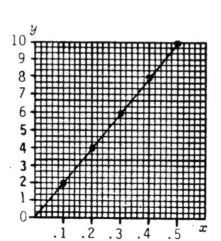

5.020 a. 3.5 $\pm$ 0.01 cm
       b. **5.6** $\pm$ 0.01 cm
       c. 2.9 $\pm$ 0.01 cm
       d. 7.6 $\pm$ 0.01 cm

5.021 adult check

5.022 Accuracy is a term used to
       describe the correctness with
       which a measurement can be deter-
       mined with a given measuring
       instrument. It is recorded as a
       $\pm$ value with each measurement.

5.023 This answer depends on the spe-
       cific careers chosen but should
       reflect Section V contents.

5.024 The examples will vary, but the
       definitions should indicate that
       qualitative is a general descrip-
       tion while a quantitative involves
       a "how much" determination.

SELF TEST 1

1.01   f

1.02   g

1.03   h

1.04   i

1.05   e

1.06   a

1.07   j

1.08   d

1.09   c

1.010   b

1.011   Either order:
     a. pure substances
     b. mixtures

1.012   Either order:
     a. elements
     b. compounds

1.013   Any order:
     a. discover universal cure
        for disease
     b. discover ways to prolong
        life
     c. transmit base metals to
        gold

1.014   Either order:
     a. English
     b. Latin

1.015   Either order:
     a. metal
     b. nonmetal

1.016 $NaBr$

1.017 CaO

1.018 Cs_2S

1.019 $MgBr_2$

1.020 K_2S

1.021 B_2S_3

1.022 Au_2S

1.023   h

1.024   e

1.025   i

1.026   d

1.027   c

1.028   b

1.029   a

1.030   j

1.031   Should summarize the paper
(report) in 1.1. This report
should be the answer key to
this question. This answer
should include:
1. Alexandria, Egypt became the
    center around A.D. 1.
2. Influence of church in Mid-
    dle Ages on science and
    alchemy.
3. Role of men like Aristotle,
    Descartes, and Roger Bacon.
4. The connection between al-
    chemy and "magic" of this
    period.
5. The definition of "puffers"
    and "adepts."

1.032   Alchemy is an ancient study of
the physical world (chemistry)
designed to discover the cure
for all diseases, prolong life,
and change base elements to
gold. Alchemy contributed to the
early studies of the properties
of common elements, symbols of
elements and compounds, and the
chemistry of single alloys.

SELF TEST 2

2.01   c

2.02   f

2.03   a

2.04   b

2.05   i

2.06   g

2.07   k

2.08   e

2.09   l

2.010   h

2.011   Either order:
        a. elements
        b. compounds

2.012   a. reactants
        b. products

2.013   Either order:
        a. pure substance
        b. mixture

2.014   Alexandria, Egypt

2.015   **Law of Constant Composition or
        Law of Definite Proportion**

2.016   II Corinthians 5:17

2.017   kinetic energy

2.018   d

2.019   b

2.020   e

2.021   c

2.022   a. C
        b. P
        c. P
        d. C
        e. C
        f. C

2.023   a. I
        b. O
        c. O
        d. O
        e. I
        f. I

2.024   a. C
        b. E
        c. E
        d. E
        e. C
        f. E

2.025   The starting materials (s) to
        a chemical reaction.

2.026   Two or more elements fastened
        together such that their indi-
        vidual identities are lost to
        an identity of a new substance.

SELF TEST 3

3.01   false

3.02   true

3.03   true

3.04   false

3.05   false

3.06   true

3.07   false

3.08   false

3.09   false

3.010   false

3.011   i

3.012   g

3.013   j

3.014   a

3.015   l

3.016   k

3.017   h

3.018   d

3.019   b

3.020   c

3.021   c

3.022   b

3.023   c

3.024   d

3.025   increasing

3.026   increasing

3.027   increasing

3.028   b

3.029   a

3.030   a

3.031   a

3.032   a. I
        b. O
        c. O
        d. O
        e. I
        f. I

3.033   a. E
        b. C
        c. E
        d. C
        e. E
        f. C
        g. C

3.034   a. Tyndall
        b. Brownian

3.035   a. homogeneous
        b. heterogeneous

3.036   Alchemy is the ancient study of chemistry that tried to link "science" with philosophy or thought. Its basic goals were to cure all diseases, change base elements to gold, and help each person to live longer. Alchemy contributed a basic foundation of common elements, their properties and symbols, knowledge of alloys, and some basic knowledge of chemistry.

3.037   Homogeneous mixtures have particle sizes that are small and similar, do not separate by natural means, and as solutions have a negative Tyndall and Brownian test. Heterogeneous mixtures can be separated by natural physical means, usually not evenly mixed, and have suspended particles that are greater than 10^{-8}cm in diameter. A homogeneous solution could be salt water; a heterogeneous mixture is fresh milk.

SELF TEST 1

1.01   i

1.02   d

1.03   a

1.04   b

1.05   g

1.06   f

1.07   l

1.08   c

1.09   k

1.010   f

1.011   j

1.012   f

1.013   o

1.014   d

1.015   m

1.016   n

1.017   d

1.018   c

1.019   h

1.020   h

1.021   a. Matter consists of tiny particles.
        b. Molecules of gas are spread out, decreasing to solids.
        c. Molecules are in rapid continued motion.
        d. Molecular collisions are elastic.
        e. Attractive forces increase as matter condenses.
        f. Temperature is a measure of average kinetic energy.

1.022   Average kinetic is the average measure of the motion energy of the system. Some molecules are moving fast, some average, and some slow.

The average of all the energies is measured by the temperature.

1.023   Evaporation is the process of molecules leaving the liquid state. When molecules have enough energy to overcome the attraction of other liquid molecules and the pressure of the atmosphere, they evaporate.

SELF TEST 2

2.01   f

2.02   e

2.03   a

2.04   a

2.05   d

2.06   c

2.07   c

2.08   g

2.09   b

2.010   e

2.011   c

2.012   b

2.013   a

2.014   e

2.015   b

2.016   a

2.017   e

2.018   c

2.019   c

2.020   e

2.021   (3 liters) (1 atm) = (x)(.62 atm)
$$x = \frac{(3 \text{ liters})(1)}{(.62)} = 4.8 \text{ liters}$$

2.022 $(3.6 \text{ liters})(1 \text{ atm}) = (x)(3.2 \text{ atm})$
$x = \dfrac{(3.6 \text{ liters})(1)}{3.2} = 1.1 \text{ liters}$

SELF TEST 3

3.01 h

3.02 i

3.03 g

3.04 j

3.05 a

3.06 b

3.07 j

3.08 k

3.09 d

3.010 b

3.011 **d**

3.012 c

3.013 c

3.014 d

3.015 e

3.016 e

3.017 d

3.018 a. -173
      b. 0
      c. -267
      d. -130
      e. 300

3.019 $(1.25 \text{ L})(0.865 \text{ atm}) = (x)(0.820 \text{ atm})$
$x = \dfrac{(1.25 \text{ L})(0.865)}{0.820} = 1.31 \text{ L}$

3.020 see 3.12

SELF TEST 4

4.01 b

4.02 d

4.03 b

4.04 c

4.05 d

4.06 a

4.07 a

4.08 d

4.09 a

4.010 a

4.011 d

4.012 d

4.013 b

4.014 b

4.015 a

4.016 c

4.017 c

4.018 c

4.019 e

4.020 a. $\dfrac{(250) \text{ ml}}{300^{\circ} \text{ K}} = \left(\dfrac{x}{350^{\circ} \text{K}}\right)$
      $x = \dfrac{(250)(350) \text{ml}}{300} = 292 \text{ ml}$
      b. Charles'

4.021 a. $\dfrac{(1.56 \text{ L})(745 \text{ mm Hg})}{300^{\circ}\text{K}} = \dfrac{(V_2)(700 \text{ mm Hg})}{373^{\circ}\text{K}}$
      $V_2 = \dfrac{(1.56 \text{ L})(745)(373)}{(700)(300)}$
        $= 2.06 \text{ L}$
      b. combined

4.022 a. $\dfrac{10\ L}{293^{0}K} = \dfrac{V_2}{373^{0}K}$ $V_2 = \dfrac{(10\ L)(373)}{293}$

$\qquad\qquad\qquad\qquad = 12.7\ L$

  b. Charles'

4.023 a. $\dfrac{(215\ ml)(1\ atm)}{293^{0}\ K} = \dfrac{(V_2)(1.5\ atm)}{273^{0}\ K}$

$\qquad V_2 = \dfrac{(215\ ml)(1)(273)}{(293)(1.5)}$

$\qquad\quad = 134\ ml$

  b. Combined

4.024 $(63.5\ ml)(735\ mm\ Hg) = (69.2ml)(x)$

$\qquad x = \dfrac{(63.5)(735\ mm\ Hg)}{69.2} = 674\ mm\ Hg$

  b. Boyles'

SELF TEST 5

5.01 e

5.02 g

5.03 c

5.04 b

5.05 a

5.06 e

5.07 d

5.08 g

5.09 g

5.010 d

5.011 b

5.012 d

5.013 c

5.014 c

5.015 d

5.016 b

5.017 a

5.018 a

5.019 d

5.020 b

5.021 a

5.022 d

5.023 c

5.024 b

5.025 b

5.026 c

5.027 d

5.028 b

5.029 d

5.030 e

5.031 3

5.032 2, 3, 2

5.033 1, 8, 10, 16

5.034 2, 6, 2, 3

5.035 H_2O

5.036 3, 4, 4

5.037 2, 2

5.038 2, 2

5.039 2, 2

5.040 2, 6, 3, 2

SELF TEST 1

1.01	d		1.027	b
1.02	c		1.028	b
1.03	i		1.029	c
1.04	e		1.030	d

1.05   i

1.06   j

SELF TEST 2

1.07   l

1.08   e   2.01   f.   Bohr

1.09   b   2.02   e.   Rutherford

1.010   e   2.03   g.   Chadwick

1.011   g   2.04   b.   Dalton

1.012   g   2.05   e.   Rutherford

1.013   a   2.06   b.   Dalton

1.014   e   2.07   c.   Thomson

1.015   k   2.08   c.   Thomson

1.016   h   2.09   a.   Democritus

1.017   c   2.010   d.   Curie

1.018   f   2.011   d

1.019   d   2.012   c

1.020   g   2.013   a

1.021   b   2.014   a

1.022   c   2.015   c

1.023   a   2.016   a

1.024   d   2.017   c

1.025   b   2.018   c

1.026   e   2.019   b

                  2.020   b

                  2.021   e

2.022 b

2.023 b

2.024 c

2.025 c

2.026 The atom is made up of layers
of electrons, something like an
onion in structure. Only
specific numbers of electrons
are possible in any particular
level.

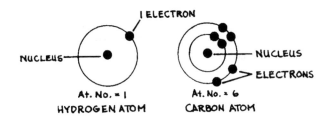

2.027 a. $1s^2$
       b. $1s^2 2s^2 2p^3$
       c. $1s^2 2s^2 2p^6 3s^2$
       d. $1s^2 2s^2 2p^6 3s^2 3p^2$
       e. $1s^2 2s^2 2p^6 3s^2 3p^6$

2.028 The orbital shapes outline the
specific geometric volumes in
which you most likely (90%
probability) will find that
type of electron.

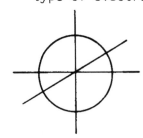

s (spherical)

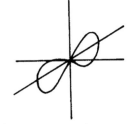

p (egg-shaped)
three sets, each shaped
alike but located on a
different axis

2.029 Valence electrons are the
electrons in the outermost
incomplete energy level. This
includes all electrons outside
the basic inert gas structure
up to the next complete inert
gas.
Examples:
He = 0
N = 5
Mg = 2
Si = 4
Ar = 0

SELF TEST 3

3.01   5

3.02   2

3.03   1

3.04   6

3.05   3

3.06   4

3.07   7

3.08   8

3.09   9

3.010 c

3.011 e

3.012 b

3.013 b

3.014 b

3.015 d

3.016 c

3.017 a

3.018 a

3.019 a

3.020   b

3.021   d

3.022   c

3.023   c

3.024   b

3.025   a

3.026   b

3.027   b

3.028   c

3.029   Examples:
    a.   atomic volume
    b.   ionization energies
    c.   boiling point, melting point
       or density

SELF TEST 4

4.01   g

4.02   i

4.03   h

4.04   n

4.05   l

4.06   f

4.07   m

4.08   a

4.09   j

4.010   b

4.011   Democritus; proposed concept of atoms

4.012   Dalton; developed atomic model of matter

4.013   Mendeleev; arranged element in Periodic Table

4.014   Thomson; discovered electron; raisin pudding atomic model

4.015   Rutherford; "open spaces" or nuclear atomic model

4.016   Bohr; developed orbital or path model of electron movement

4.017   Schrodinger; developed wave or quantum, model of electron structure

4.018   Chadwick; discovered the neutron

4.019   c (b may be correct if the student considers the bonding state valence electron configuration.)

4.020   a

4.021   a

4.022   a

4.023   d

4.024   a

4.025   a. $^{76}_{34}Se$
     b. $^{229}_{90}Th$
     c. $^{0}_{-1}e$

4.026   a. $1s^2 2s^2 2p^6 3s^2 3p^3$
     b. $1s^2 2s^2 2p^6 3s^2 3p^6 4s^2 3d^{10} 4p^3$

4.027   Examples:
    a.   as a source of energy to produce electricity
    b.   as a source of research in agriculture
    c.   to treat and cure cancer
    d.   to date objects in archeology
    e.   to determine and measure cell production in plants and animals

4.028   The Bohr model has electrons
        located in specific rings (shells)
        around the nucleus.

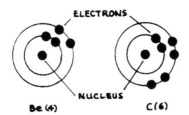

4.029   The spectral lines are produced
        when high energy electrons
        (excited electrons) fall back
        down to their stable positions
        closer to the nucleus. When
        the electrons move from
        orbital to orbital back toward
        the nucleus, energy is released
        at each jump and shows up as
        light. The patterns and energy
        of light released give evidence
        as to the internal structure
        of each atom.

4.030   Hint:
        Answer should show logic and
        should be based on fact as much
        as possible. Specifics are
        necessary to illustrate quality
        of thinking.

SELF TEST 1

1.01   +2

1.02   a. +1
        b. -2
        c. +3
        d. +2
        e. -1
        f. 0

1.03   c

1.04   c

1.05   e

1.06   b

1.07   c

1.08   d

1.09   a

1.010   d

1.011   a

1.012   c

1.013   a. $Ca(OH)_2$
        b. Na_2SO_4
        c. $AlPO_4$

1.014   a. +3
        b. +1
        c. $\pm$4
        d. -3
        e. +1
        f. +1 or -1
        g. -1
        h. -2
        i. 0

1.015   +2

SELF TEST 2

2.01   f

2.02   c

2.03   d

2.04   f

2.05   a

2.06   a

2.07   a

2.08   a

2.09   d

2.010   e

2.011   a

2.012   c

2.013   c

2.014   a

2.015   a

2.016   d

2.017   a

2.018   c

2.019   b

2.020   a

2.021   a. 67
        b. 22
        c. 39
        d. 51
        e. 0
        f. 4

2.022   a. 1. similar electronegativity
              values
           2. highly directed bond
           3. sharing bond - valence
              electrons are shared between
              nuclei
           4. common in organic compounds
           5. mostly nonmetal - nonmetal
              bond

b. 1. dissimilar electronegativity
   values
2. directed bond
3. one atom takes the electron
   of the other
4. common in inorganic compounds
5. mostly metal - nonmetal bond
c. 1. made of metal atoms only
2. high conductive bond
3. mobile, "loose" electrons
4. metal - metal bond
5. not very common naturally
   occurring bond

SELF TEST 3

3.01   m

3.02   l

3.03   r

3.04   n

3.05   t

3.06   u

3.07   o

3.08   p

3.09   q

3.010   d

3.011   a

3.012   a

3.013   a, b, c, g, h

3.014   a

3.015   b

3.016   a

3.017   c

3.018   d

3.019   d

3.020   c

3.021   c

3.022   c

3.023   a.

3.024   a

3.025   c

3.026   a

3.027   c

3.028   d

3.029   a

3.030   a. 4%
        b. 47%
        c. 6%
        d. 12%
        e. 22%
        f. 43%

3.031   1. made from ions
        2. very strong
        3. found in most metal-nonmetal
           bonds
        4. most mineral (inorganic) bonds
           are ionic
        examples: NaCl, $CaCl_2$

3.032   1. sharing bond
        2. directed
        3. makes up most organic compounds
        4. mostly nonmetal-nonmetal bonds
        examples: H_2O, CO_2, NO_2

3.033   1. very nondirected bond -- mobile
           electrons
        2. metal-metal bond
        3. communal sharing of valence
           electrons among several atoms
        4. strong bond -- not common
           naturally
        examples: Ag, Au

SELF TEST 1

1.01   true

1.02   false

1.03   false

1.04   true

1.05   true

1.06   false

1.07   true

1.08   false

1.09   false

1.010   true

1.011   b

1.012   c

1.013   c

1.014   d

1.015   a

1.016   b

1.017   b

1.018 $x + y$

1.019   endothermic

1.020   given off

1.021   increased

1.022   a. $\Delta H = -22,000$ cal
        b. $\Delta H = -331$ kcal
        c. $\Delta H = +2.4$ kcal
        d. $\Delta H = -712$ kcal
        e. $\Delta H = +94.50$ kcal

1.023   26.4 kcal/mole carbon

1.024
C–H	99	C=O	-192
C–H	99	C=O	-192
C=O	192	O–H	-111
O–O	119	O–H	-111
	+509		-606

$\Delta H = -97$ kcal/mole CH_2O

SELF TEST 2

2.01   true

2.02   false

2.03   false

2.04   true

2.05   false

2.06   a

2.07   d

2.08   e

2.09   c

2.010   f

2.011   a

2.012   b

2.013   e

2.014   d

2.015   a

2.016   d

2.017   c

2.018   d

2.019   b

2.020   b

2.021   B

2.022 endothermic

2.023 B

2.024 activation energy

2.025 releases (loses)

2.026 $C_2H_6 + \frac{7}{2}O_2 \rightarrow 2CO_2 + 3H_2O$

C-H 6 x 99 = 594
O-O $\frac{7}{2}$ x 119 = 416.5
C-C 1 x 83.1 = $\underline{83.1}$
1093.6

C=O (4 x -192) = -768
O-H (6 x -111) = $\underline{-666}$
-1434.

$\Delta H = -340.4\frac{kcal}{mole} C_2H_6$

2.027

Normal Activation Energy

The positive catalyst lowers the normal activation complex energy level by providing an alternate pathway for the reactants to react together.

SELF TEST 3

3.01 true

3.02 false

3.03 false

3.04 true

3.05 true

3.06 true

3.07 false

3.08 false

3.09 true

3.010 true

3.011 c

3.012 c

3.013 a

3.014 d

3.015 c

3.016 a

3.017 e

3.018 d

3.019 b

3.020 d

3.021 a

3.022 d

3.023 a

3.024 c

3.025 activation complex

3.026 products

3.027 catalyst

3.028 Law of Chemical Equilibrium

3.029 activation energy

3.030 LeChatelier's Principle

3.031   O–H   2 x 111   =   222
        C–H   6 x 99   =   594
        C–O   2 x 84   =   168
        O–O   3 x 119   =   <u>357</u>
                              1341
        C=O   4 x   (-192)   =   -768
        H–O   8 x   (-111)   =   <u>-888</u>
                              -1656

ΔH = -1656 + 1341 = -315 kcal
produced/2 moles CH_3OH

3.032 $\dfrac{[HSO_4^{-1}]}{[H^+][SO_4^{-2}]}$

3.033 $C_2H_4 + 3O_2 \rightarrow 2CO_2 + 2H_2O + 331.6$
kcal

SELF TEST 1

1.01   b. NH_4^+
       e. $H_2PO_4^-$
       f. H_3O^+

1.02   a. $CaCl_2$
       b. $AlCl_3$
       c. K_2S
       d. Li_2S
       e. $AlCl_3$

1.03   a. CsF
       b. $AlCl_3$
       c. KI

1.04   a.   carbon tetrachloride
       c.   distilled water

1.05   b.   0.8 M

1.06   b.   When ionic character decreases, electrical conductivity decreases.

1.07   b. SrF_2

1.08   a. NH_3
       b. CH_2F_2
       c. H_2S
       d. NaI
       e. $NaCl$
       f. NH_3
       g. NH_3
       h. NaF
       i. $BrCl$

1.09 $$\begin{array}{l} 2 - H = 1 \times 2 = 2 \\ \underline{1 - O = 16 \times 1 = 16} \\ \qquad g.f.w. = 18 \end{array}$$

1.010 $$\begin{array}{l} 3 - Ca = 40 \times 3 = 120 \\ 2 - P = 31 \times 2 = 62 \\ \underline{8 - O = 16 \times 8 = 128} \\ \qquad g.f.w. = 310 \end{array}$$

1.011 290 g
       $$5.0\ M = \frac{5\ moles}{liter}$$
       $$= (5)(58\ g) = \frac{290\ g}{liter}$$

1.012 5.8 g
       $$0.1\ M = \frac{0.1\ mole}{liter}$$
       $$= (0.1)(58\ g) = \frac{5.8\ g}{liter}$$

1.013 true

1.014 true

1.015 false

1.016 false

1.017 false

1.018 true

1.019 Any order:
       a.   concentration (molarity)
       b.   electrical nature of the substances
       c.   potential number of ions

1.020 a.   solvent
       b.   solute

1.021 2, 1, 2

1.022 1, 2, 1, 2

SELF TEST 2

2.01   b. Hg_2^{+2}
       c. PO_4^{-3}
       e. HCO_3^-
       g. Al^{+3}

2.02   a. NaF
       b. $MgCl_2$
       c. AlF_3
       d. $BaCl_2$

2.03   a.   ions

2.04   c. $0.1\ M\ CaCl_2$

2.05   b.   2 moles of ions

2.06   e.   size of container

2.07   c.   produces more ions

2.08   b.   that it has an equal number of protons and electrons

157

2.09   a. increases

2.010   b. NaI is less ionic in bond character

2.011   c. 27.8 g

2.012   saturated

2.013   Any order:
   a. the nature of the solvent
   b. temperature
   c. degree of pulverization
   d. amount of agitation (stirring)

2.014   precipitate out the excess KNO_3

2.015 $[Pb^{+2}][Cl^-]^2$

2.016 $2AgNO_3 + MgCl_2 \rightleftharpoons 2AgCl + Mg(NO_3)_2$

2.017 $2Na - 2 \times 23.0 = 46.0g$
   $2S - 2 \times 32.0 = 64.0g$
   $3O - 3 \times 16.0 = 48.0g$
   Total g.f.w. $= 158.0g$

2.018 $K_{sp} = [Ag^+][Cl^-] = 1.0 \times 10^{-16}$

   $[Ag^+] = \dfrac{K_{sp}}{[Cl^-]} = \dfrac{1. \times 10^{-16}}{[1 \times 10^{-8}]} =$

   $= 1 \times 10^{-8}M$

SELF TEST 3

3.01   true

3.02   false

3.03   false

3.04   true

3.05   true

3.06   true

3.07   false

3.08   false

3.09   false

3.010   true

3.011   k

3.012   g

3.013   j

3.014   i

3.015   a

3.016   b

3.017   f

3.018   e

3.019   c

3.020   h

3.021   d. a proton donor

3.022   a. 32.6 g

3.023   b. 30 ml

3.024   c. 7

3.025   b. 1×10^{-11}

3.026   a. 1×10^{-10}

3.027   e. 0.01 N

3.028   e. 2.0 M

3.029   b. neutral

3.030   c. slightly acidic

3.031   saturated

3.032   Any order:
   a. nature of the solvent
   b. temperature
   c. pulverization
   d. agitation

3.033   Any order:
   a. sour taste
   b. turns blue litmus red
   c. reacts with metals to give hydrogen
   d. contains hydrogen

3.034   compound formed as a product of the reaction of an acid and a base

3.035   pH

3.036

$$3 - Ca = 3 \times 40.0 = 120.0$$
$$2 - P = 2 \times 31.0 = 62.0$$
$$\underline{8 - 0 = 8 \times 16.0 = 128.0}$$
$$\text{g.f.w.} = \text{Total} = 310.0g$$

3.037 $K_{eq} = \dfrac{[CO_2][H_2O]^2}{[CH_4][O_2]^2}$

3.038   10 g = ¼ mole of NaOH

$$M = \frac{\text{moles}}{L} = \frac{0.25 \text{ moles}}{0.50 \text{ L}}$$
$$= 0.50 \text{ M}$$

SELF TEST 4

4.01   false

4.02   false

4.03   true

4.04   false

4.05   true

4.06   b

4.07   b

4.08   e

4.09   b

4.010   b, $BaCO_3$; d, $Fe(OH)_3$; e, $PbCl_2$; g, $Ca_3(PO_4)_2$

4.011   c

4.012   c

4.013   d

4.014   b

4.015   a

4.016   c

4.017   b

4.018   98 grams

4.019   Any order:
     a. it is sour to the taste
     b. has hydrogen ions
     c. reacts with metals
     d. turns litmus red

4.020   the product of neutralization of an acid and a base

4.021   Any order:
     a. type of solvent
     b. potential number of ions
     c. concentration
     d. ionic character of solute

4.022   ions

4.023   increases

4.024   +6

4.025   pH

4.026   0.01 moles = 0.585 g

4.027

$$Zn \rightleftharpoons Zn^{+2} + 2e^-$$
$$2e^- + Cu^{+2} \rightleftharpoons Cu^0$$
$$\overline{Zn + Cu^{+2} \rightleftharpoons Zn^{+2} + Cu^0}$$

$$+0.76$$
$$\underline{+0.34}$$
$$+1.10 \text{ volts}$$

4.028
a. pH = 4 = $[10^{-4}]$
     $[H^+] = 10^{-4}$ M
b. pOH + pH = 14
     pOH + 4 = 14
     $\therefore$ pOH = 10

4.029 $BaC_2O_4 \rightleftharpoons Ba^{+2} + C_2O_4{}^{-2}$

$$\frac{0.093 \text{ g}}{225 \text{ g}} = 4 \times 10^{-4} \text{moles } BaC_2O_4$$
$$K_{sp} = [Ba^{+2}][C_2O_4{}^{-2}]$$
$$= [4 \times 10^{-4}][4 \times 10^{-4}]$$
$$= 1.6 \times 10^{-7}$$

SELF TEST 1

1.01   false

1.02   false

1.03   true

1.04   false

1.05   false

1.06   false

1.07   true

1.08   c

1.09   d

1.010   a

1.011   b

1.012   e

1.013   Any order:
        a. construction (buildings)
        b. paper
        c. heat (energy)

1.014   thousands

1.015   Either order:
        a. hydrogen
        b. carbon

1.016   Any order:
        a. coal
        b. petroleum
        c. plant and animal products
           or natural gas

1.017   a. 1
        b. 2
        c. 1
        d. 2

1.018   a. 2
        b. 3
        c. 4
        d. 3

1.019   a. 2
        b. 1
        c. 2

1.020 C_2H_6

1.021 C_9H_{20}

1.022 $C_{11}H_{24}$

1.023 $C_{16}H_{34}$

1.024 $C_{20}H_{42}$

1.025 $C_{32}H_{66}$

1.026 $C_{150}H_{302}$

SELF TEST 2

2.01   true

2.02   true

2.03   true

2.04   **true**

2.05   false

2.06   true

2.07   true

2.08   false

2.09   false

2.010   false

2.011 $1s^2\ 2s^2\ 2p^2$

2.012   Any order:
        a. amorphous
        b. graphite
        c. diamond

2.013   tetrahedral

2.014   covalent

2.015   hybridization

2.016 sp^3

2.017   a

2.018   a

2.019   a

2.020   b

2.021   b

2.022   c

2.023   a. 2
        b. 7
        c. 4
        d. 6

2.024   a. 2
        b. 1
        c. 2

2.025   a. 3
        b. 2
        c. 3
        d. 4

2.026   Any order:
        a. coal
        b. petroleum
        c. plant and animal products
           or natural gas

2.027   IV A or IV

2.028   six

2.029   four

2.030   three

SELF TEST 3

3.01   I

3.02   O

3.03   I

3.04   I

3.05   O

3.06   a

3.07   b

3.08   b

3.09   c

3.010   a

3.011   Any order:
        a. amorphous
        b. diamond
        c. graphite

3.012   Any order:
        a. buildings
        b. heat (energy)
        c. paper

3.013   Any order:
        a. petroleum
        b. coal
        c. plant and animal products
           or natural gas

3.014   substitution (combustion)

3.015 C_nH_{2n}

3.016   c

3.017   b

3.018   d

3.019   a

3.020   b

3.021 c

3.022 d

3.023 a

3.024 b

3.025 f

3.026 1; 2; 1; 2

3.027 1; 3; 2; 2

3.028 2; 5; 4; 2

3.029 Any order:
     a. hardness
     b. three dimension
     c. nonconductivity

3.030 Any order:
     a. softness
     b. good conductivity
     c. planar shape

SELF TEST 1

1.01   false

1.02   true

1.03   true

1.04   true

1.05   false

1.06   HCl

1.07   calcium

1.08   moth balls

1.09   food chain

1.010   double

1.011   e

1.012   f

1.013   a

1.014   c

1.015   b

1.016   Example:

Reaction Coordinate

1.017 $C_2H_6 + 6Cl_2 \rightarrow C_2Cl_6 + 6HCl$

1.018   a. 1
          b. 1
          c. 1
          d. 1

1.019   a. 1
          b. 1
          c. 1

1.020   a. 1
          b. 2
          c. 1

SELF TEST 2

2.01   d

2.02   g

2.03   a

2.04   b

2.05   c

2.06   e

2.07   true

2.08   false

2.09   true

2.010   true

2.011   false

2.012   false

2.013   true

2.014   false

2.015   true

2.016   Examples; any order:
          a. ethyl
          b. methyl (wood alcohol)
          c. isopropyl (rubbing alcohol)

2.017   water (H_2O)

2.018   Examples; any order:
          a. acetic
          b. formic
          c. butyric

2.019   oxygen

2.020 d

2.021 c

2.022 a

2.023 b

2.024 1, 1, 1, 1

2.025 2, 1, 2, 2

2.026 1, 3, 2, 3

2.027 2, 5, 4, 4

2.028 1, 3, 1

SELF TEST 3

3.01 j

3.02 f

3.03 e

3.04 g

3.05 a

3.06 i

3.07 k

3.08 c

3.09 b

3.010 d

3.011 substitution

3.012 addition

3.013 peptide (amide)

3.014 ammonia

3.015 Either order:
a. carbon dioxide
b. water

3.016 aldehydes

3.017 false

3.018 true

3.019 false

3.020 true

3.021 true

3.022 false

3.023 true

3.024 true

3.025 false

3.026 false

3.027 b

3.028 c

3.029 d

3.030 a

3.031 c

3.032 Examples; any order:
a. formic
b. acetic
c. butyric

3.033 Examples; any order:
a. methyl
b. isopropyl
c. butyl

3.034 Example:
1. All proteins naturally occuring are made from left-handed amino acids.
2. The probability of life (protein synthesis) by random chance is too small to be a possible explanation to life.

3.035 a. 2
b. 1
c. 2
d. 2

3.036 a. 1
       b. 3
       c. 2
       d. 3

SELF TEST 1

1.01   d

1.02   c

1.03   i

1.04   e

1.05   i

1.06   j

1.07   l

1.08   e

1.09   b

1.010   e

1.011   g

1.012   g

1.013   a

1.014   e

1.015   k

1.016   h

1.017   c

1.018   f

1.019   d

1.020   g

1.021 1.386×10^{-2}

1.022 6.528×10^{7}

1.023 $0.1696 = 1.696 \times 10^{-1}$ or
        $0.1697 = 1.697 \times 10^{-1}$

1.024 7.8744×10^{4}

1.025 4.802×10^{1}

1.026   true

1.027   false

1.028   false

1.029   true

1.030   false

1.031   true

1.032   false

1.033   true

1.034   true

1.035   a. phase
        b. chemical
        c. chemical
        d. chemical
        e. chemical
        f. chemical

1.036   a. inorganic
        b. inorganic
        c. organic
        d. organic
        e. inorganic
        f. organic

1.037   a. mixture
        b. mixture
        c. mixture
        d. pure
        e. pure
        f. mixture

1.038   a. element
        b. compound
        c. compound
        d. compound
        e. element
        f. compound

1.039   d

1.040   b

1.041   c, d, f, h

1.042   c

1.043 e

1.044 d

1.045 b

1.046 a. 12%
       b. 22%
       c. 47%
       d.   6%
       e. 43%
       f.   4%

1.047 c

1.048 b

1.049 a

1.050 d

1.051 e

1.052 e

1.053 d

1.054 b

1.055 a

1.056 e

1.057 c

1.058 d

1.059 44 g

1.060 160 g

1.061 80 g

1.062 74 g

1.063 84 g

1.064 142 g

SELF TEST 2

2.01 g

2.02 f

2.03 l

2.04 b

2.05 h

2.06 a

2.07 k

2.08 j

2.09 e

2.010 c

2.011 a

2.012 d

2.013 b

2.014 e

2.015 a

2.016 c

2.017 a

2.018 b

2.019 a

2.020 B

2.021 endothermic

2.022 B

2.023 activation energy

2.024 releases

2.025 a. $+ {}^{4}_{2}He$
       b. $+ {}^{0}_{-1}e$

2.026 a. +3
       b. +1
       c. ±4
       d. -3
       e. +1
       f. +1
       g. -1

h. -2
i. 0

2.027 a. $Ca(OH)_2$
       b. Na_2SO_4
       c. $AlPO_4$

2.028 a. +1
       b. -2
       c. -1

2.029 true

2.030 false

2.031 true

2.032 false

2.033 false

2.034 true

2.035 true

2.036 true

2.037 false

2.038 2; 1; 2

2.039 1; 2; 2

2.040 2H = 2 x 1 = 2
       0 = 1 x 16 = 16
          g.f.w. = 18 grams

2.041 3 Ca = 3 x 40 = 120
       2 P = 2 x 31 = 62
       8 0 = 8 x 16 = 128
          g.f.w. = 310 grams

2.042 the nonwater product of the
       reaction between an acid and
       a base

2.043 Any order:
       a. concentration
       b. conductivity
       c. potential ions

2.044 Cu^{+2}

2.045 donates

SELF TEST 3

3.01   d

3.02   d

3.03   b

3.04   c

3.05   e

3.06   a

3.07   f

3.08   d

3.09   a

3.010 c

3.011 c

3.012 b

3.013 a

3.014 b

3.015 e

3.016 c

3.017 a

3.018 d

3.019 c

3.020 b

3.021 e

3.022 c

3.023 d

3.024 d

3.025 c

3.026 c

3.027 c

3.028 a

3.029 a

3.030 c

3.031 a

3.032 c

3.033 d

3.034 a

3.035 d

3.036 a

3.037 d

3.038 a

3.039 e

3.040 b

3.041 c

3.042 e

3.043 activation complex

3.044 products

3.045 catalyst

3.046 k_{eq}

3.047 activation energy

3.048 Le Chatelier's Principle

3.049
$$
\begin{array}{l}
2 \times 3 \ \text{C-H} = 6 \times \ \ 99 = \ \ \ \ 594 \\
2 \times 1 \ \text{C-O} = 2 \times \ \ 84 = \ \ \ \ 168 \\
\underline{3 \times 1 \ \text{O-O} = 3 \times 119 = \ \ \ \ 357} \\
\text{needed} = 1,119
\end{array}
$$

$$
\begin{array}{l}
2 \times 2 \ \ \ \ \text{C=O} = 4 \times 192 = \ \ \ \ 768 \\
\underline{4 \times 2\text{-}2 \ \text{O-H} = 6 \times 111 = \ \ \ \ 666} \\
\text{lost} = 1,434
\end{array}
$$

$$
\Delta H = 1,119 + (-1,434) \\
\ \ \ \ \ \ = -315 \ \text{kcal}
$$

3.050 $\dfrac{[HSO_4^{-1}]}{[H^+] \ [SO_4^{-2}]}$

3.051

3.052 g

3.053 i

3.054 e

3.055 b

3.056 c

3.057 d

3.058 f

3.059 k

3.060 j

3.061 h

3.062 Either order:
a. amines
b. amides

3.063 primary

3.064 Either order:
a. amino acids
b. peptide (amide)

3.065 ketone

3.066 water

3.067 formic acid

3.068 true

3.069 true

TEST KEYS

1. f. ml

2. h. $\pm$ 0.2

3. i. quantitative

4. a. **milli**

5. j. hypothesis

6. k. kilogram

7. b. cm

8. c. instrument of volume

9. g. xy = k

10. d. centi

11. c. mm

12. a. $\pm$ 0.1 ml

13. a. 6.02×10^6

14. a. **law**

15. d. 0.000391

16. b. ml

17. d.

18. d. ml

19. c. $\pm$ 0.05

20. c. ml

21. inverse

22. hypothesis

23. law

24. $\pm$ 0.1 mm

25. accuracy

26. 1.386×10^{-2} or 1.4×10^{-2}

27. $6.528 \times 10^7 = 6.5 \times 10^7$

28. 1.697×10^{-1}

29. $7.8744 \times 10^4 = 7.87 \times 10^4$

30. 4.802×10^1

31. teacher check

32. Sample data
    a. 1; 12
    b. 2; 6
    c. 3; 4
    d. 4; 3
    e. 6; 2

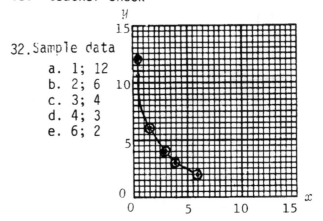

33. Hint:
    Comparisons should clearly show
    that quantitative observations
    involve a "how much" while a
    quantitative does not.

34. Example:
    The chemical technician is
    responsible for the laboratory
    tests, analysis, and quality checks
    on products and production of a
    product. This career links the
    theoretical with the practical
    application.

35. A hypothesis is an "educated"
    guess as an explanation to a set
    of data or phenomena. A hypothesis
    may or may not be true, and several
    hypotheses may explain the same
    observations.
    (Example: My hypothesis is that the
    drought caused this tree to die.)

1. true

2. false

3. false

4. true

5. false

6. false

7. true

8. false

9. true

10. true

11. a. phase
    b. chemical
    c. chemical
    d. chemical
    e. chemical
    f. chemical

12. a. I
    b. I
    c. O
    d. O
    e. I
    f. O

13. a. m
    b. m
    c. m
    d. p
    e. p
    f. m

14. a. E
    b. C
    c. C
    d. C
    e. E
    f. C

15. a

16. c

17. b

18. d

19. d

20. c

21. a. pure
    b. mixture

22. Either order:
    a. metal
    b. nonmetal

23. Either order:
    a. hydrogen
    b. oxygen

24. Alchemy is a blend of science, magic, and religion that flourished about 300 B.C. in Alexandria, Egypt.
    Purposes: (Any order)
    1. discover universal cure for disease
    2. discover a means to prolong life
    3. transmute the base elements, like lead, into gold
    Contributions: (Any order)
    1. properties of common elements
    2. many symbols
    3. study and characteristics of common alloys

25. Definitions:
    Heterogeneous mixtures can be separated by physical means, homogeneous can not. Heterogeneous particle size is greater than 10^{-8}cm's.
    Examples:
    Heterogeneous includes colloids (sols & gels) and suspensions. Homogeneous includes solutions and alloys.

1. d

2. d

3. b

4. c

5. e

6. a

7. a or f

8. d

9. a

10. c

11. b

12. c

13. c

14. d

15. c

16. c

17. a

18. e

19. a

20. e

21. d

22. a

23. b

24. a

25. c

26. c

27. d

28. 1, 1, 1, 1

29. e

30. c

31. b

32. a

33. e

34. c

35. d

36. b

37. c

38. 44 = (12 + 2 x 16)

39. 63.5 + 32. + (4.) (16) = 159.5

40. 14 + 4 + 14 + 3(16) = 80

41. 40 + 2(16 + 1) = 74

42. 27 + 3(19) = 84

43. (23)2 + 32 + 4(16) = 142

44. 32g CH_4 = 2 moles

   2 moles CH_4 → 2 moles CO_2

   2 moles CO_2 = (22.4 L/mole)(2 moles)

   $\qquad$ = <u>44.8 L</u>

45. 32g CH_4 = 2 moles

   2 moles CH_4 → 4 moles H_2O

   4 moles H_2O = $\left(\dfrac{18g}{mole}\right)$(4 moles) = <u>72 g</u>

1.	g	13.	b
2.	f	14.	b
3.	l	15.	b
4.	b	16.	b
5.	h	17.	e
6.	a	18.	c
7.	k	19.	a
8.	j	20.	d
9.	e	21.	c
10.	c	22.	e
11.	c	23.	e
12.	e	24.	c

25. Democritus ,460 B.C.; proposed concept of atoms

26. Dalton ,1766; developed atomic model of atoms

27. Thomson ,1856; discovered the electron; "raisin pudding" atomic model

28. Curie, 1867, discovered, isolated, and named radioactive elements.

29. Rutherford ,1871; "open spaces" model or nuclear model of atoms

30. Bohr ,1885; developed quantum (energy) path of electrons

31. Schrodinger ,1887; developed quantum model; probability model of atoms

32. Chadwick ,1891; discovered the neutron

33. a. $^{4}_{2}He$

    b. $^{0}_{-1}e$

34. a. $1s^2 2s^2 2p^6 3s^2 3p^1$
    b. $1s^2 2s^2 2p^6$
    c. $1s^2 2s^2 2p^6 3s^2 3p^6 4s^2$

35. Answers should include:
   1. Concept of lack of exactness in locating the specific position of electrons.
   2. 90% probability of electron location
   3. orbitals
   4. nuclear model with mass concentration in center
   5. nature of electrons, protons, and neutrons

36. a. The Bohr model has electrons located in specific rings (shells) around the nucleus.

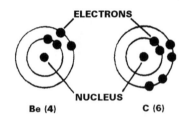

b. The spectral lines are produced when high energy electrons (excited electrons) fall back down to their stable positions closer to the nucleus. When the electrons move from orbital to orbital back toward the nucleus, energy is released at each jump and shows up as light. The patterns and energy of light released give evidence as to the internal structure of each atom.

1. a

2. c

3. f

4. h

5. i

6. k

7. m

8. o

9. q

10. s

11. d

12. b

13. c, d, f, h

14. c

15. e

16. d

17. b

18. c

19. b

20. a

21. b

22. d

23. d

24. d

25. a. 12%
    b. 22%
    c. 47%
    d. 6%
    e. 43%
    f. 4%

26. c

27. b

28. a

29. d

30. e

1. true

2. false

3. true

4. true

5. false

6. false

7. true

8. true

9. true

10. false

11. b

12. d

13. k

14. c

15. h

16. a

17. f

18. e

19. i

20. g

21. a

22. b

23. d

24. b

25. d

26. activation complex

27. endothermic

28. LeChatelier's Principle

29. heat of reaction

30. equilibrium

31.
$$C-H \quad 4 \times 99 \quad = 396$$
$$O-O \quad 2 \times 119 \quad \underline{= 238}$$
$$+ 634$$

$$C = O \quad 2 \times (-192) = -384$$
$$H - O \quad 4 \times (-111) = \underline{-444}$$
$$-828$$

$$\underline{\Delta H = -194}$$

32.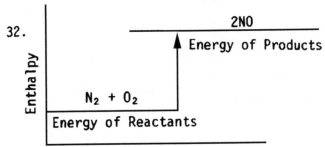

33. Example:
A catalyst interacts with the reactants to change the pathway (mechanism) for the reaction so that the activation energy requirement is decreased. Enzymes, metals, and rough surfaces serve as good catalysts.

1.   true

2.   true

3.   false

4.   true

5.   false

6.   d.   0.450 M

7.   a. 1.34×10^{-3}

8.   d.

9.   a.   Presence or absence of ions.

10. d

11. c.   50 ml

12. e

13. b

14. c

15. e

16. Any order:
     a.   temperature
     b.   type of solvent
     c.   pulverization
     d.   stirring

17. the product of neutralization of
     an acid and a base

18. Any order:
     a.   concentration
     b.   ionic character
     c.   potential number of ions

19. Cu^{+2}

20. donates

21. a.   +1
     b.   -2
     c.   -1

22. No reaction possible
     $$Sn \rightarrow 2e^- + Sn^{+2} \qquad 0.14$$
     $$\underline{Fe^{+2} + 2e^- \rightarrow Fe \qquad -0.44}$$
     $$-0.30$$

1. I

2. 0

3. I

4. 0

5. 0

6. h

7. c

8. f

9. i

10. a

11. e

12. b

13. d

14. k

15. g

16. C_nH_{2n-2}

17. $1s^2\ 2s^2\ 2p^2$

18. C_nH_{2n+2}

19. covalent

20. C_nH_{2n}

21. Any order:
    a. petroleum
    b. coal
    c. plant and animal products
       or natural gas

22. alkene

23. addition

24. tetrahedral

25. alkane

26. 2; 7; 4; 6

27. 2; 9; 6; 6

28. 1; 4; 3; 2

1. g

2. i

3. e

4. b

5. c

6. d

7. f

8. k

9. j

10. h

11. Either order:
    a. amines
    b. amides

12. primary

13. Either order:
    a. amino acids
    b. peptide (amide)

14. ketone

15. water

16. Example:
    formic acid

17. true

18. true

19. true

20. false

21. a. 1
    b. 3
    c. 2
    d. 3

22. a. 2
    b. 1
    c. 2
    d. 2

23. Examples; any order:
    a. butyl
    b. isopropyl
    c. methyl

24. Either order:
    a. improbability of the chemicals getting together
    b. left-handed nature of proteins from living things

1.	k	27.	h
2.	g	28.	b
3.	e	29.	i
4.	h	30.	c

5. a

6. i

7. c

8. b

9. f

10. d

11. true

12. true

13. false

14. true

15. false

16. c

17. e

18. c

19. b

20. d

21. a

22. b

23. e

24. f

25. a

26. g

31.

$$2C_2H_6 + 7O_2 \rightarrow 4CO_2 + 6H_2O$$

$$
\begin{aligned}
\text{C-H} &= 12 \times 99 = 1{,}188 \\
\text{O-O} &= 7 \times 119 = 833 \\
\text{C-C} &= 2 \times 83 = 166 \\
&\quad \text{gained} = +2{,}187 \text{ kcal} \\
\text{C=O} &= 8 \times 192 = 1{,}536 \\
\text{O-H} &= 12 \times 111 = 1{,}332 \\
&\quad \text{lost} = -2{,}868 \text{ kcal}
\end{aligned}
$$

Net $\Delta H = +2{,}187 + (-2{,}868) = -681$ kcal

1. g

2. k

3. h

4. j

5. a

6. i

7. c

8. d

9. b

10. e

11. b

12. c

13. b

14. c

15. a

16. d

17. a

18. a

19. d

20. d

21. Examples:
    a. production
    b. research and development
    c. product development or marketing, management, safety engineers, environmental engineers, information chemists, or chemical technicians

22. direct

23. $1.6648 \cdot 10^{-2}$

24. $3.19 \cdot 10^{-4}$

25. ± 0.01 ml

26. Answer depends on objects chosen by teacher.

27. $3.58 \cdot 10^{0}$

28. $1.746 \cdot 10^{2}$

29. Sample answers:
    a. 3, 3
    b. $6, \frac{3}{2}$
    c. $\frac{3}{2}, 6$
    d. 9, 1
    e. 1, 9

1. true

2. false

3. false

4. false

5. false

6. true

7. false

8. true

9. false

10. true

11. a. phase
    b. physical
    c. physical
    d. chemical
    e. phase
    f. chemical

12. a. inorganic
    b. organic
    c. organic
    d. inorganic
    e. organic
    f. inorganic

13. a. mixture
    b. pure
    c. mixture
    d. mixture
    e. pure
    f. mixture

14. a. compound
    b. element
    c. element
    d. compound
    e. compound
    f. element

15. a. C
    b. D

16. a. A
    b. B

17. F

18. a. D
    b. E

19. c

20. b

21. d

22. e

23. f

24. Evaluate this answer against the student's answer to Activity 1.1 in the LIFEPAC.

25. Example:
    Heterogeneous mixtures can be separated by physical means, homogeneous cannot. Heterogeneous particle size is greater than 10^{-8} cm. Heterogeneous includes colloids (sols and gels) and suspensions. Homogeneous includes solutions and alloys.

1. h

2. i

3. j

4. d

5. k

6. e

7. b

8. a

9. f

10. g

11. c

12. d

13. a

14. d

15. c

16. a

17. b

18. d

19. a. 18
    b. 330
    c. 188
    d. 40
    e. 170

20. 2

21. a. 4
    b. 2
    c. 2

22. a. 2
    b. 2
    c. 2

23. 22.4 liters

24. 446 grams

1. f

2. d

3. j

4. i

5. a

6. b

7. c

8. g

9. k

10. h

11. d

12. b

13. c

14. a

15. a

16. c

17. d

18. b

19. c

20. d

21. ^4_2He

22. $^{248}_{96}\text{Cm}$

23. $1s^2 2s^2 2p^6 3s^2 3p^5$

24. $1s^2 2s^2 2p^6 3s^1$

25. $1s^2 2s^2$

26. calcium

27. **argon**

28. neon

29. **silver**

30. phosphorus

1. d

2. e

3. a

4. c

5. b

6. d

7. c

8. d

9. a

10. a

11. b

12. c

13. a

14. a

15. c

16. 63%

17. 6%

18. 19%

19. 34%

20. 63%

21. ionic

22. metallic

23. covalent

24. ionic

25. covalent

26. metallic

27. nonpolar

28. polar

29. nonpolar

30. polar

1. i

2. d

3. a

4. g

5. k

6. c

7. f

8. b

9. h

10. e

11. gas formation

12. enthalpy

13. released

14. equilibrium

15. Any order:
    a. concentration
    b. temperature
    c. pressure

16. returns

17. catalysts

18. negative

19. H-H 2 x 104 = +208
    O-O   119   +119
                    ─────
                    +327

    H-O 4 x-111 = -444

    ΔH = -117

20.

21. a. energy of reactants
    b. activation energy
    c. energy of products

1. e

2. f

3. d

4. b

5. **a**

6. g

7. c

8. k

9. **j**

10. i

11. c

12. b

13. c

14. d

15. d

16. c

17. **b**

18. a. 2,   b. 1,   c. 1

19. a. 1,   b. 2,   c. 2

20. a. $1 \cdot 10^{-2}$ M
    b. yes
    c. Example:
    $$[Ag^+][Cl^-] = [1 \cdot 10^{-2}][1 \cdot 10^{-5}] = 1 \cdot 10^{-7}$$

    $K_{sp} = 1.7 \cdot 10^{-10} < 1 \cdot 10^{-7}$ so a precipitate will form

1. h

2. i

3. k

4. f

5. d

6. a

7. e

8. g

9. c

10. j

11. Any order:
    a. petroleum or natural gas
    b. coal
    c. animals and plants

12. Any order:
    a. graphite
    b. diamond
    c. amorphous

13. $1s^2 \; 2s^2 \; 2p^2$

14. a. 4
    b. 2
    c. 4

15. a. 7
    b. 4
    c. 6

16. a. 3
    b. 2
    c. 2

17. C_nH_{2n-2}

18. C_nH_{2n}

19. C_nH_{2n+2}

20. inorganic

21. organic

22. organic

23. inorganic

24. organic